ʹIVING
ONIA

EDU⁴

CARMINE L PETRANGELO

D1614973

website: survivingdystonia.com
pet5654@embarqmail.com
Ph: 352-637-5654
CP Publishing

239075221

I wish to acknowledge the following:
The illustrations on pages, 6, 14, 18, 63, 64, and 134 are reprinted by permission of Harper Collins Publishers 10 E. 53rd Street New York, New York.
The illustration on page 141 reprinted with permissions from The Cleveland Clinic Foundation, copyright 2002, 9500 Euclid Ave. NA311 Cleveland, Ohio

The illustrations on pages, 72, 88, 94, 106, and 122 were created by, Linsay Poulin an art student from, Central Florida Community College in Citrus County Florida. I would also like to thank Mr. Cletus from the library department of Central Florida Community College for his assistance in the production of this book.

I would like to thank Lee Cloward for his assistance in proofreading and editing.
A special thanks too Terry Arnston for her advice in producing this book.
Professional editing by Susan Kelley, Beachcomberbooks.com.
The books cover design provided by Jonathan Gullery from HSA Design. JG@midcity.net

ISBN Number: 0-9723711-0-9

Table of Contents

4

Dedicated to all those who suffer from dystonia.

Preface

This book is about an illness that is quite rare. It is an illness that is greatly misunderstood by many in the medical field. Those who have this illness, or any rare illness, suffer not only from the debilitating effects of the illness, but also from a lack of understanding from those in the medical field as well as from relatives and friends. Because of this lack of understanding, those of us who suffer from such illnesses are often forced to suffer alone.

The illness I am writing about is called dystonia. I have this illness. This is the personal story of my struggle in life with this disorder. It is my sincere hope that sharing my story will help provide for the readers of this book an understanding of how blessed they are to be able to live through life without disabling illnesses such as I and many others have.

Twenty-two-year-old David, in whom dystonia twisted his back, produced involuntary movements of his pelvis, and incapacitated him physically and socially.

INTRODUCTION

This book is about a rare form of an illness called dystonia. I have had this illness since I was seven years old. Dystonia comes in many different forms. The form I have is called Dystonia Musculorum Deformans. Today this form of dystonia is more commonly called, Generalized Dystonia. It is referred to as an early onset dystonia because it develops at a very early age. It is one of the worse forms of dystonia because it eventually affects the entire body. It is a movement disorder with some similarities to Parkinson's disease.

What happens in Generalized Dystonia is a gradual loss of control of many different muscles of the body. This usually begins with a specific limb moving involuntarily because of a muscle spasm caused by the dystonia.

In my case, my first symptom of dystonia involved walking. My normal walking gait became abnormal. Other people saw the difference but in the beginning I thought I was walking normally. Over time, the abnormal gait became more obvious until even I noticed it. Yet at that point of dystonia's development, I was normal in every other way.

As time passed, my abnormal walking became even more obvious. I also began falling down, tripping myself up by the leg most affected by the dystonia. As time passed, I developed another symptom of this form of dystonia. My left ankle began to curve inward. Soon afterward, my right foot began to kick my left ankle as I walked.

As the disease progressed, I began to experience involuntary movements while sitting. My back would twist from involuntary movements in my lower back; my right shoulder would also move, as would my right arm. Eventually, I began kicking my left ankle with my right foot whenever I attempted to move my right leg. This became so common over time that it actually caused a bruise to develop on my left ankle on occasion.

Another problem developed when the twisting motion started in my back. The right side of my body would often twist to the left while I was sitting down. To counter that, I positioned my elbows on top of my desk at school to hold my body in place. To offset the problem of my right foot kicking my left ankle, I fixed my feet to the floor or to the frame of the desk with muscles I could control, to keep my body in position. I had to do all this literally every day.

Further on, this book will give a more detailed view of how I battled to control my body. I will describe what it is like to have an illness as rare as this and how I am forced to cope with it every day. I will write about its progression and how my everyday life changed as the illness worsened. I will describe how I battled to try to live a normal life with this disease. I will describe my deep pain over the ten years it took to properly diagnose it.

I will describe one doctor's amazing conclusion when he accused me of faking my illness to get attention. I will describe how I was forced to survive alone as a result of this misdiagnosis for six long years.

This book points out some criticism of the medical profession and the reasons for this criticism. My intent is not to criticize all of the medical profession for the mistakes made by those in my story. My intent is to communicate to the medical profession how important their jobs are and how much their carelessness or their big egos can affect a little boy's life, as described in this story.

CHAPTER 1
(The early years)

I was like everyone else before I was seven years old. I can remember going to Tiogue Lake with my mother and my older brother Dale when I was five. I practiced diving into the water. It was usually a belly flop but it was fun. I walked and ran like everyone else. The lake was about a mile away from where we lived in Coventry, Rhode Island. It was a very popular spot for the people who lived nearby.

My brother and I fought a lot and my mother would punish us for it. Sometimes when we were in bed at night, we would make a lot of noise and my mother would get really mad. She would come into our room with a belt and hit us with it. It would hurt. So we would cover ourselves with the blanket and when my mother started hitting us, we acted like it was hurting us. It worked quite well. She really thought she was hurting us.

I was a typical little boy. I wanted to play in sports like baseball and basketball. I had friends in the neighborhood. They did not seem to be bothered by my medical problem after it developed.

We rented the house we lived in. It was a duplex with one apartment on one side and another on the other side. The people on the other side were the landlords. They had a horse on the premises and for a while they had a small bull. I occasionally helped the landlord's children clean the horse's stall. Sometimes they let me ride the horse.

I started school when I was six years old. That was when my first problem was discovered. I had trouble hearing the teacher and I did poorly in 1st grade. I was shy and was afraid to tell the teacher I could not hear her.

At the age of six, I realized I was deaf in my left ear. I told no one. The school gave hearing tests when I was in 1st grade. I could not hear anything when they tested my left ear. They could not understand why I could not hear in the left ear so they decided to retest it. I did not want them to know I could not hear in the left ear so I faked hearing the noise they turned on when testing me.

When they tested for hearing, they used a sequence of sound, then no sound. I had to raise my hand every time I heard a sound. I had figured out the sequence they used so I raised my hand each time I knew they played a sound, even though I did not hear anything when they tested the left ear. It worked! I passed with flying colors.

It was of course a mistake to do that. I could not hear the teacher and I flunked 1st grade. When I took the test the following year, I did not try to hide my hearing problem. It was discovered my hearing loss was present at birth. There was nothing they could do about it. While it was a problem to me at times, I never considered it a serious handicap. The hearing in my right ear was so good it made up somewhat for being deaf in the left ear.

We had to wear special uniforms to school. They consisted of light blue shirts with dark blue ties and dark blue pants. I liked dressing up in the uniforms.

In those days, the teachers in Catholic school were called nuns or sisters. The nuns were different from public school teachers. They were much stricter with their rules. They had little clappers made of wood. If someone was disobedient, they threatened to hit the student with those clappers on the knuckles. I cannot remember if that was ever done to anyone but I am sure it hurt.

I was a student in 1st grade in Catholic school when the dystonia began to show development. I was not the first one to notice it; my mother was. My mother, my brother Dale and I were walking down the street in the business district of Arctic in West Warwick, Rhode Island. My mother yelled at me to walk straight. I could not understand what she meant because I thought I *was* walking straight. We were walking in an area that was about a mile and a half from where we lived in Crompton.

This happened more and more frequently as I got older. Slowly, but surely, things worsened. My mother continued to yell at me to walk straight. I was so confused. I was just a little boy. I could not walk the way my mother wanted me to. I tried so hard.

10

It is difficult for me to remember details about the development of my dystonia at that time. I was too young to take any specific notice of anything wrong. I may have experienced some small development of movements while sitting but it was not significant enough for me to notice. Yet my mother noticed my walking problem even though I did not.

I cannot explain why I did not notice the walking problem at that time. Since I could not see myself when I was walking, it makes sense that I was not able to observe anything wrong in the early stages. Furthermore, I think any young child would have difficulty noticing something odd in his development because such a young child would find it difficult to judge what was normal or abnormal unless it was something very obvious.

My first year in Catholic school was pretty good. I remember being very shy. I do not remember anyone noticing or saying anything to me about my walking. My grades were average but I progressed well in my studies.

In 2nd grade, my schoolwork improved even more. I was pulling B average grades in most of my classes. While I still felt relatively normal, the abnormal walking was slowly getting worse.

I developed a good friendship with a classmate named Larry Poulin. He was a slightly heavyset individual whose friendship would be of great value and assistance in my time of need. He would eventually come to my aid as my illness worsened.

By the time I reached 3rd grade, the dystonia was beginning to affect my walking enough for me to notice it for the first time. At this stage of the illness although walking was difficult to me, I still felt fairly normal. My parents were now becoming very concerned about my walking.

We were poor so they could not afford the kind of medical care I needed. In Rhode Island, where we lived, Rhode Island Hospital had a clinic for poor families. My parents decided to take me to that clinic, located in Providence, the capital of Rhode Island. Specialists and other doctors saw patients at the clinic for a very small fee. That allowed poor people to get medical care they otherwise would have been unable to receive. Rhode Island Hospital should be commended for establishing this clinic.

We lived about 12 miles from the clinic. We always took the bus to Providence. It was a long ride to a little boy. The clinic was in one of the hospital's older buildings. Although we were told to be at the clinic by 9:00 A.M., the doctors never arrived until after 10:00 A.M. or sometimes after 11:00 A.M. We sat on long wooden seats similar to the ones found in church. After waiting an hour or longer to see a doctor, those wooden seats became very uncomfortable. The patients at the clinic were poor like us. Many were children with their mothers, just like I was.

The building had a very high ceiling. There was no elevator in the building only a stairway in each section. A long hallway separated the sections.

I went to many different doctors at the clinic. I saw orthopedic doctors of all kinds and many other doctors whose specialties I cannot remember. It was always the same thing: I was asked to walk down the hallway a few times, then my mother would take me home after making an appointment to come back to the clinic in a few months. I would visit this clinic for many years before I would be properly diagnosed.

My walking had deteriorated to the point where short walks were normal but longer walks were becoming more difficult. Being so young, I did not really feel handicapped by this developing problem then. However, that would soon change.

We had two recesses during the school day at St. Vincent de Paul Catholic School. Near the end of 3rd grade, my dystonia had progressed to the point where I needed assistance getting back to class from recess. It was Larry Poulin who assisted me by allowing me to lean on him. I could make it alone if I had to, but I could not keep up with my classmates. I hated to burden Larry but he did not seem to mind.

I would go bike riding sometimes with Larry and another friend, Robert Grenier. We would ride to Tiogue Lake in Coventry, Rhode Island together and just hang out. Sometimes we would go to the

12

lemonade stand and have lemonade. I was doing the normal things young boys did at my age.

A Thirty-six-year-old woman totally incapacitated by abnormal postures and movements of far advanced dystonia.

14

CHAPTER 2

As a little boy, it was not easy for me to understand what was happening to me. I wanted to do all of the things other little boys wanted to do. As the illness progressed, my walking was becoming more and more difficult.

We continued to visit the clinic at Rhode Island Hospital. The routine was the same. We got there early and sometimes waited hours before we could see the doctor. It was always the same result; the doctors could not figure out what was wrong. We went back home on the bus and waited for the next appointment.

The first time I started to feel the movements from the dystonia was at the beginning of 4th grade. While sitting, I would squirm around in my seat a lot. I noticed that my right leg would move without my wanting it to. It was difficult for a ten-year-old boy to understand what was going on. I just did what I had to do to stabilize myself in my chair.

By that time, I had been maintaining very good grades in school. I was a B+ student. When we took special aptitude tests, I always did well. They tested us on our spelling and definitions of words. I always scored equivalent to an 8th or 9th grade level while still in 4th grade. I was proud of that.

Larry Poulin was still assisting me at recess by allowing me to lean on him to stabilize myself when I went back and forth. The nuns in the school allowed that. At that point of my schooling, no one ever talked to me about my problem or what kind of help I might need getting around. Thank God I had Larry Poulin!

In the schoolyard, there was a game that used a post cemented in the pavement; the post's top had a string tied to it with a ball the size of a soccer ball attached to the string's other end. I cannot remember the name of the game. Its object was to hit the ball with a closed fist past the other guy, causing the string to wrap around the post. I played that game during recess. The dystonia did not appear to affect me very much while playing it.

Except for Larry Poulin and Bob Grenier, I did not have too many friends in school. One thing I learned as a child with a disability was that my classmates tended to ignore me for the most part. I talked with some of them but I did not hang around with them because I could no longer get around well enough to keep up with them.

I accepted the situation for what it was and tried to live as normally as possible. There was nothing I would not try to do if it interested me. I was a normal little boy with a developing medical problem.

While I had trouble walking, I could still run. I still do not know why that was the case. Perhaps it was because running used a lot more muscle force than walking. At any rate, I was glad I could still do that.

Early in the spring of 4th grade, I decided I wanted to try out for the Little League. I loved playing baseball. I never thought about my walking problem because I knew I could run. I filled out the Little League application form; then I began practicing for the tryout. I was not a very big person so I could not hit the ball that far. My fielding was not too bad but it certainly needed work. I thought practice would help me to improve.

We practiced at a field about half a mile from my house. There were usually about five or six of us. I had to walk to get there. While it was difficult to walk there to play baseball, running was not a problem when actually playing baseball. Yet that would soon begin to change.

I did not do too badly in the beginning. I got my share of hits and my fielding improved with every practice session. I really could see my improvement.

I realize now that I was not good enough for Major League but I was a good candidate to get a spot on a farm team.

At a time when my spirits were up and my dreams ran sky high, something odd happened. In the beginning, it did not happen every time but it progressed to the point that every time I swung at the ball,

16

I fell down. I can remember to this very day how frustrated I felt every time that happened.

At almost the same time, I also started falling down when running to first base. I can remember how odd that seemed to me. Within a month or so, I gave up my dream to play in the Little League as I realized I was beginning to lose my ability to run.

As troubling as my difficulty to walk had been, this new development was a crushing blow to me. It was the first time I realized my problem was serious. It was having a much broader impact on my everyday life because my running was deteriorating also. That was very difficult for a ten-year-old boy to face.

As time passed, I continued to deteriorate. I was more aware of my illness than ever before. I realized it made me different from normal kids. Before I thought of myself as normal and I could put my illness aside but now I began to realize I was not normal and things were getting tougher for me to handle. Stumbling and falling while running was now an everyday occurrence. For the first time in my life, I began crying myself to sleep.

A nine-year-old boy, the son of the woman in the preceding picture, has noted the beginning symptoms of dystonia in his left arm.

CHAPTER 3

That summer I spent a lot of time around the area of Tiogue Lake. There was a spot in a more secluded area other than the two beaches where my friends and I spent some time. While I could not swim, we often went there. While I had trouble walking, it did not stop me from doing a lot of the things other kids did. I could still ride a bicycle and that was how my friends and I got to Lake Tiogue.

Earlier, I mentioned how my mother had taken my brother and me to one of Lake Tiogue's beaches when I was younger. At that time, I loved the water and was never afraid to dive in. However, two things happened that changed things dramatically. The first was when I started having dreams of drowning in a nearby pond. I do not know why I had such a dream but I did. The other was the dystonia itself. Because swimming required me to be relaxed, the muscle spasms I suffered because of the dystonia made it impossible for me to relax the way the average person did when swimming.

Sometimes someone would have an inner tube to float on when we visited Tiogue Lake and I would frequently use it to move around in the water. It was fun. As much as I would have liked to be able to swim like everyone else, I was content with staying near shore or floating on an inner tube.

One time, my brother Dale, my older cousin Poncho and I went fishing at Tiogue Lake. My cousin's real name was Anthony. I do not know where the name Poncho came from but that was what we called him. At that time, we lived near Tiogue Lake. My walking was pretty poor that day. I stumbled often, with my right leg kicking my left ankle on occasion. I kept falling behind my brother and my cousin, sometimes forcing them to slow down and wait for me.

I do not remember catching any fish that day but as we went back home, I was struggling considerably while walking. I was carrying my fishing pole on my shoulder. What I did not realize was that the hook had come off the line guide on the pole and was dangling near the back of my right knee.

As I hobbled along, my right leg tripped up my left leg and caused me to fall. The hook at the end of my fishing line then lodged into the back of my right knee. The hook's barb was firmly imbedded so we had to go home with it still stuck in me. My mother realized there was no way to get the hook out so she rushed me to the nearest doctor's office. The doctor had to stick a needle in my knee to numb the area so he could safely and painlessly remove the hook from the back of my knee, which he did.

As stated earlier, one of the ways I got around during this period was by riding my bicycle. I cannot tell you how important that bicycle was to me. With the walking problem getting worse, it provided a way of getting to places that were almost impossible for me to get to otherwise.

However, even riding a bicycle was difficult because of the effects of dystonia. My right leg was the main problem. It would frequently slip off the pedal, sometimes causing me to fall off the bicycle. Between falling down while walking and falling off the bicycle, I sustained bruises and cuts too numerous to count.

Sometimes my pants leg got caught in the chain of the bicycle, causing me to fall. On one occasion when this happened, I fell hard to the ground and banged my head on the pavement, causing a small gash in my head that bled quite badly. I remember going to the hospital, where I received four stitches to close the wound. Things like this were getting to be routine for me at this point of my life.

CHAPTER 4

I was 11 years old when I started 5th grade. I was still attending St. Vincent de Paul School. My grades in school continued to be good. At this point, the dystonia did not affect me in my scholastic studies. I also continued to get high scores in the special testing for spelling and definitions. I was well above 5th grade level in these areas and among the top three in my class. I was proud of that. I enjoyed learning and began to read more often.

I particularly liked the Hardy Boys books. There were about 20 of this series of books at the local library. In the books, their father was a detective and they constantly were getting involved in mysterious adventures. Like their father, they tracked down criminals, often times getting themselves into difficult situations. The books were so rich with adventure and intrigue that I found myself feeling as if I were there.

I also liked the Nancy Drew stories. They were similar to the Hardy Boys books but involved a teenaged girl named Nancy Drew. Nancy Drew books were geared a little more toward girls but the adventures were very similar. They were good clean reading for young people at the time.

Larry Poulin was still helping me in getting outside for recess as well as helping me get back inside. The dystonia was still progressing. I had developed a little more difficulty in sitting than a year earlier. In particular, my left leg seemed to want to move on occasion whether I wanted it to or not. It was not enough to warrant any special concern on my part. I learned to deal with it. Yet as time progressed, that would change.

During my visits to the clinic, they occasionally performed X-rays to explore the possibility that something in my bone structure might be causing my problem. On one particular X-ray visit, the technician asked me to lie on top of the X-ray table.

21

This can be a problem for a patient suffering from certain forms of dystonia. In my case, I suffer from what they called in those days Dystonia Musculorum Deformans. In this form, movements affect many parts of the body. However, keep in mind that I had not yet been diagnosed with dystonia during all of these experiences.

When I got on top of the X-ray table, I discovered there was no way to counter the movements from my dystonia because I did not have anything to grab onto. In my everyday life, I could always find different ways to support myself. If I was in a chair, I could move around and shift my body to counter the involuntary movements. Oftentimes, I could brace myself against the frame of the chair; using the muscles I had control of to counter the muscles I could not control. I could also grab something on the chair to support myself, as well as moving my body back and forth to counter the involuntary movements.

While atop the X-ray table, I tried my best to control my involuntary movements. My body was all over the place, making it very difficult to get a good X-ray. The technician took the X-rays but I knew he was angry with me. Being just a little boy, I had no idea what was going on and I did not know what to say to him.

During another clinic visit early in my fifth year of school, I was asked to have an X-ray done again. I was worse at this point than when the other X-ray was taken. While lying on the X-ray table, my body was really twitching. There were two female technicians trying to take the X-ray. Since they could not keep my body still, they called in another X-ray technician. It turned out to be the one who had gotten angry with me when he did the first X-ray a year or so earlier.

When he showed up, he looked at me and said, "I've had this little bastard before." He then proceeded to restrain me by holding my shoulders down while one of the others held down my legs. After a combined effort of the three technicians, they finally were able to take the X-ray they needed. Incidents like this were so hard to take because I was trying so hard to do what they asked of me. I was so hurt by this incident that I can remember going to my room when we got home and crying my eyes out. I have never told anyone about this before.

22

I cannot remember whether this was the X-ray that showed I had a slight spinal curvature. I have had so many that it is hard to remember which X-ray was which. I do remember it was around this time that an X-ray showed such a curvature. Yet at the time, the doctors did not consider this discovery significant since it was only a slight curvature.

I continued to do well in my scholastic work. Larry Poulin and I were still friends and he was still assisting me when I needed it. He made things a lot easier for me with his help. Larry Poulin and Bob Grenier were still the only close friends I had at school at the time.

Bob Grenier was a heavyset person who would go bike riding with me on occasion. Although a big guy, he was not very athletic. When we went on bike rides, he always had trouble making it up big hills. He had little physical endurance. I of course had dystonia and that was always creating a challenge to me in anything I did.

The age of 11 was to be a dramatic turning point in my life with dystonia. While at that stage of my life I had been forced to endure many unpleasant experiences, I had at least been able to lead a relatively normal life. I was not able to do a lot of the things I really liked to do but I did not let the effects of dystonia keep me from living. However, events were about to happen, one of which would leave a scar on my life that still exists today.

The first event was a combination of two occurrences that in some ways were similar. The first occurrence happened in the living room of the home we rented on Congdon Street in Coventry. One day out of the clear blue, as I stood in the living room, it suddenly looked sideways. In other words, my viewpoint of the room changed from normal to about a 45-degree angle. This scared me so much that I ran crying in fear to my father. I cannot remember how long it lasted but it happened about half a dozen times and to this day I cannot explain it. At about this same time, the second occurrence happened. I started experiencing dizzy spells. They were not frequent but they frightened me. Also, I discovered that when I spun myself around I got dizzy much more quickly than before.

To this day, that is still the case. I do not know if this has any link to my dystonia. The answer to that rests with the experts who study this disease.

The other event took place on one particular visit to the clinic. I had an appointment to see a doctor by the name of Dr. John Strom, a neurologist. On this scheduled appointment, we were running about an hour late. Just as we came into the area of the clinic where the doctors met with their patients, Dr. Strom passed us. He was leaving just as we were walking in to see him. Since we did not know what he looked like and he did not know what we looked like, the appointment never materialized. This was to be the irony of an amazing circumstance that would have a profound effect on my life.

After missing the appointment with Dr. Strom, we made another return to the clinic to see another doctor. It was at this appointment that my life was to take a dramatic turn for the worse. The doctor I saw that day asked me to walk down the hallway. He then asked me to walk down the hallway again. One of the strange things about my walking problems was that I could sometimes walk short distances and look normal. At this stage of the development of my dystonia, I had not progressed to the most serious level.

This doctor came to a remarkable conclusion. Based on my ability to walk down the short hallway with a relatively normal gait, he decided I was faking the walking problem to get attention. This inevitably created a whole new level of problems for me that would turn my life upside down.

In reflecting back on this particular doctor's conclusion, a very obvious question stands out. How could one doctor make such a bold conclusion based on so little information in such a short period of time?

I cannot remember what my parents thought because I have no memory of any conversation with them about this. I only remember my reflections about the doctor's conclusions. To begin with, at 11 years of age I looked at adults as not capable of making mistakes about things like this. In my reasoning as an 11-year-old boy, I simply never thought of questioning a doctor's decision. After all, he went to college and he was an adult. How could he possibly be wrong?

24

In accepting this doctor's analysis, one very big thought developed in my mind. Why would I put myself through so much pain and suffering to get attention? In my mind, this simply did not make sense. Yet at the same time I thought that, I still believed he had to be correct in his conclusion. After all, doctors never made mistakes.

After about four years of visiting the clinic at Rhode Island Hospital, my problem appeared to have been diagnosed. The question was, 'What happens now?' The answer to that was quick. An appointment was made for me to return to the clinic to begin seeing a psychiatrist.

My first appointment to see the psychiatrist was in the early spring of my fifth year of grammar school. I walked into the psychiatrist's office at the clinic and sat down. The psychiatrist was about forty, balding and a bit overweight. I do not remember what was said at this first meeting other than that the psychiatrist was asking a number of personal questions.

The second visit was more interesting. Somehow, the clever psychiatrist had gotten us into talking about my mother and how she would swear all the time and that her swearing sometimes annoyed me. (If you heard my mother's swearing, it would upset you too.) During this conversation, the dystonia was bothering me and I was moving around in the chair, trying to get comfortable. The dystonia had progressed to the point that at times it was very difficult to sit in a chair. Seeing me move around like that, the psychiatrist said, "I see it troubles you when we discuss your mother's swearing."

That statement had a profound affect on me. It was as if I had suddenly become an adult. I realized the psychiatrist had mistakenly interpreted my moving around in the chair as meaning something other than what was really causing it. He was wrong! Now I realized maybe the other doctor was also wrong.

There was a third and final visit to the psychiatrist. I actually cannot remember very much about that meeting. It was short. The psychiatrist was angry with me and began yelling at me. I cannot remember what he said. I only remember that he was upset while I was quite calm. I left his office and went home with my mother, not knowing that the psychiatrist was going to make a recommendation that would forever leave an emotional scar on my life.

I was now near the end of 5th grade and I was looking forward to being out of school and enjoying the summer. The dystonia was progressing. Sitting down was becoming more and more uncomfortable. This was becoming a bigger and bigger annoyance to me. It was a constant struggle trying to find a comfortable position in my seat at school.

Standing straight was also a problem. I had to shift my weight back and forth, trying to stabilize myself and to offset the effects of the muscle spasms caused by the dystonia. Leaning against something worked although it was still uncomfortable. I was still relying on Larry Poulin when we were at recess. I would lean on him or a tree or the fence around the schoolyard to stabilize my body and counter the effects of the dystonia. It was difficult but it was the only way I could function.

After the last visit with the psychiatrist, I returned to school, unaware that something dramatic was about to take place in my life. Apparently, the doctors had decided they would force me to stop my "faking of illness to get attention" by ordering everyone to stop assisting me in getting around in my everyday life. I assumed both the psychiatrist and the doctor who had first made that amazing diagnosis in a five-minute physical had made this recommendation.

No one told me about this. No doctor told me I would no longer receive any help. My parents never told me either. I learned the hard way.

At school, the nuns were apparently instructed to make sure I no longer received any help at recess or at any other time during the school day. I learned about this at recess near the end of 5th grade. When recess ended, I did what I had been doing for well over a year. I leaned on my friend Larry for support so I could get back to class with everyone else. As soon as the nun saw this, she immediately instructed Larry not to assist me, telling him I would have to get back to class on my own.

Without Larry's support, I of course did what I had to do; I hobbled to the wall of the school to keep from falling down. The nun

26

did not stop there; she yelled at me to walk on my own and to stand straight. I pushed off the wall and tried to walk alone but stumbled and fell bruising my knee. Still there was no assistance. I struggled back to the wall and pulled myself up again and proceeded to do my best, using the wall of the school to get back to class. By the time I got back to the classroom, I was out of breath. I took my seat.

It did not end there. We always started the school day with the Morning Prayer, which the entire class stood up to say. The dystonia had progressed to such a point that it was difficult for me to stand up straight. I had to shift the weight of my body from side to side, using the muscles I could control to offset those I could not. It was very difficult to do and required a lot of concentration on my part. We were also required to hold our hands folded together in front of us while reciting the prayer. Now the nuns yelled at me every morning to stand straight. I felt so humiliated. I would try so hard to satisfy them but there was no way I could overcome the effects of the dystonia on my body.

At recess I could no longer rely on Larry's help. I still leaned on him when I could but we were always yelled at when the nun in charge saw us. I realized I would have to get back to class on my own. I always had that ability but I could not do it and also be back in class at the same time as my fellow classmates, which I was supposed to do.

Without Larry's help, I would never get back in class on time again. When recess would end, everybody would go back to class while I did what I had to do. I would hobble to the wall of the school and use it as support to get back inside. I would then use the banister on the stairway to prop myself up so I could get to the second floor where my classroom was located. As I walked into the room, everyone would already be seated and all eyes would be on me as I struggled to my seat. The nun would give me a look of disapproval when I sat down. This would happen every single school day from then on.

It did not really matter how much yelling or criticism I received; the dystonia had its own life within my body and I could only do the best I could do to survive with it. No amount of punishment could hurt me as much as having dystonia did.

Now the school, my parents, and other relatives were all told I was faking illness to get attention. I was faced with the reality that I was now on my own. I now had to begin a strategy to survive. Obstacles that would be overwhelming to any 11-year-old boy now surrounded me.

CHAPTER 5

The 5th grade came to an end and a new summer was upon us. I did not let the new development interfere with my need to live. Away from school, I was away from the criticism and embarrassment that now existed there. Yet nothing appeared to have changed my relationship with my friends during the summer. We still visited Tiogue Lake.

Near the lake was a Dairy Queen ice cream parlor that I enjoyed visiting with my friends. The ice cream was very good. They also sold hot dogs. Whenever I had the money, I loved getting a hot dog there. There was also a miniature golf course adjacent to the Dairy Queen and I liked to watch the people there. The only real estate agent in Coventry owned the miniature golf course. His daughter was one of my classmates at St. Vincent de Paul School.

My main mode of travel was still my bicycle. I could not walk well enough to get around the area without it. I still struggled with my feet slipping off the pedals but I could tolerate that and I was not about to let my illness take riding my bicycle away from me. The bicycle gave me freedom to live and enjoy life.

I was 12 years old when I started 6th grade in September. The nuns continued to keep Larry Poulin from assisting me in returning to class at the end of recess. They also continued to tell me to stand straight while reciting Morning Prayer before the start of every class. It bothered me a lot but I had no control over the situation. They were convinced I was faking and were determined to make me accept it. In a way, I wish they had been right. The humiliation of having an illness that so distorts the body and takes away dignity as dystonia does is more than any person should ever have to experience.

The particular nun I had, as a teacher in 6th grade seemed a less pleasant individual than any of the other nuns in the school. When we stood up for prayer in the morning, she would fold her arms in front of her and raise them up while looking at me, indicating that I should stand straight. It really made me feel very uncomfortable to go through this every single morning. I still had to deal with going to and coming back from recess. It caused an unwarranted shame to develop in my mind.

On occasion, we were asked to speak on a subject before the class. We were usually asked to stand and read from a book. My teacher sat me in a seat close to the front of the class around the middle of the room. I feared being asked to stand and read, knowing it would draw attention to me and that everyone would see me trying to control the involuntary movements caused by my illness.

One day, the teacher asked me to stand and read from the book at my desk. It was bad enough being asked to stand and read, but to hold a book was asking too much.

Whenever I held a book in my hands, my body would always want to move to the right. At home, I could find different ways of reading that were more comfortable. If I read in a chair, I could usually brace my body against the back of the chair to stabilize myself, or I could lie on my bed and change positions to counteract the effects of the muscle spasms created by the dystonia.

Standing next to my desk in class to read significantly limited what I could do to counter the movements from the dystonia. I stood up with the book in my hands and began reading what the teacher had asked me to read. As I did, my arm rose up and I could feel my body twisting to the right. I tried to stabilize my body by flexing the muscles I could control and using that force to keep my body under reasonable control. I struggled to read the book because my attempt to stabilize myself in a standing position caused my arms and hands to shake and made the movement from the dystonia very visible. While I was an exceptional reader, under those conditions I stumbled through the reading because of the effort I had to make to stabilize myself.

The worse experience was the one time the nun asked me to stand in front of the class and read. I faced the entire class. I struggled through the reading but the agony and humiliation was brutally cruel even though the intentions may have been good.

30

During the school year, every so often we would walk to Saint Vincent de Paul Church for religious instruction. The church was about a mile from the school. So I was then forced to walk one mile to the church without any assistance.

We all lined up for the walk and I was placed at the end of the line. They set us up in pairs and we began the walk. I did my best but I was falling behind my other classmates. As I started walking, I fell to the ground. I can remember that my lunchbox, which I was carrying in my right hand, flew in the air and fell just ahead of me. I got back up, started walking again and fell further and further behind the other students. I could only walk short distances before the effects of the illness caused me to lose control, stumble and fall.

The nuns finally gave in to me and sent two students to stay with me while the others continued on to the church. The two students were instructed to stay with me but otherwise not to assist me. I made the one-mile trip but was exhausted by the time I reached the church. This would happen again and again every time we made the one-mile trip to the church.

The way they were treating me seemed so cruel. All I could do was survive. With the dystonia worsening, combined with the constant humiliation to which I was being subjected in school, I found myself feeling totally alone. I cried alone. I prayed alone. I was ashamed of myself because of the way I walked. I cried many nights. I asked God to please make me better. I cried and asked God, "Why me?"

My shame came from not being able to walk normally like the other kids. As the illness worsened, there was a point at which I began staying in the house in seclusion. I got so pale from staying inside that my older brother started calling me Whitey.

There was no one to turn to because they said I was faking the illness to get attention. There was nothing I could do but suffer alone as the progression of the illness slowly sapped away at my everyday activities, making them more and more difficult. I continued to cry alone and prayed to God to make me better.

I finished my sixth year at St. Vincent de Paul School. In spite of the entire emotional trauma I experienced in 6th grade, I still managed to get good grades.

Before my 13th birthday, we moved to West Warwick, Rhode Island into a four-family apartment building. It was not much but we were poor and it was the best we could do. While the main apartment was on the first floor, my bedroom was on the third floor.

I made a number of new friends in the neighborhood. Milton Eastman was one of them. He lived up the road about 300 feet from my house. I also met Joseph Andrewchow. The three of us hung out together quite a lot. They did not seem to be bothered by my difficulty with walking. I then met Henry, who had a Polish name; I could not spell it then and I am not about to try spelling it now.

There was a baseball field and a Babe Ruth league field nearby so the four of us would frequently visit the fields and play a little ball or just hang out. I could not do very well any more because of the progression of the dystonia but I did what I could.

Moving to West Warwick meant attending a new school. My mother and father enrolled me in West Warwick Junior High. I was back in public school again. On my first day, I was placed in class 7-7. There were seven different classes in 7th grade, based on previous grades in grammar school.

In other words, the best students were placed in class 7-1. The worse were placed in 7-7. The reason I was placed in 7-7 was because some of the stronger kids were in this class and the school was concerned about how I would be able to get around in school. Unlike Catholic school, junior high had six different classes spread out over the school day and each class was located in a different classroom. We started the day in what they called homeroom.

There were a lot more students in this public school than there were in the Catholic school. The thing I liked most about junior high was that no one yelled at me to stand straight, nor did they force me to do things I could not do.

I do not know to this day why that stopped but I was glad it did. I found my way to my homeroom on the first day of school. It seemed so different from Catholic school. I no longer had to wear a school

32

uniform. We had a homeroom teacher. He seemed like a pretty decent guy. The school was larger than the Catholic school. It held the 7th, 8th and 9th grades.

On the first day, they handed out our course schedules of six different classes. A different teacher taught each class. My homeroom teacher was to teach us geography. It was going to be a long walk to many of my classes from my homeroom. It was going to be a challenge getting from one classroom to the next.

Now at the age of 13, I was becoming much more interested in girls. I could not help noticing how many attractive girls we had in our homeroom. My favorite was Elizabeth Brazil. I thought she had such a pretty face.

The bell rang for us to go to our first class. My first class was down the hall, a pretty long walk for me. I used the walls to get to the class. I ended up doing that for every class. It was a challenge.

The teachers could see how difficult it was for me to get around on my own. They assigned a couple of the other students in my homeroom class to assist me in getting from class to class. I appreciated the help but it was embarrassing to know everyone would see me being carried from one class to another. They usually had one guy hold me up on one side while the other held me up on the other side. They pretty much dragged me to class.

Life went on like this for a while until one day my mother and father came to pick me up from school at the end of the day. My homeroom teacher instructed two of my fellow students to assist me to my parents' car. My parents were absolutely appalled to see me being assisted from the school that way. My mother gave me a firm scolding because it embarrassed her to see me like that.

I doubt she could have been as embarrassed as I was to have her scold me in such a way. Nor could she have been as embarrassed as I was about being carried from one class to the next with so many people watching me. I was deeply hurt by her reaction. I cried myself to sleep that night. Yet as hurt as I was, I still loved my mother.

As an adult now, I am sure my parents never intended to hurt me. It must have hurt them to see their son like that and to feel so helpless to assist him.

33

The next day I refused the assistance of any of my classmates to help me from classroom to classroom. When they did try to assist me, I brushed them aside. I had made a decision. Never again would I ever allow myself to be embarrassed the way I had been the day before. From that day on, I got to my classrooms on my own with no one else's help. It was difficult, but that was the way I wanted it.

The school had a gym class. I went down to gym class and watched my fellow classmates work out. I wanted to participate but there was no physical way I could do that. I accepted the situation as I had accepted similar situations so many times before.

While the dystonia had so limited me in getting from classroom to classroom and in participating in gym class, it did not affect my schoolwork. After six years in a Catholic school, I found the schoolwork in a public junior high school easy.

I excelled in my first semester. I made the honor roll, receiving first honors. I had the second highest grades in my homeroom class. My grades were all A's, with a few B's. The work seemed so easy to me that I could not understand how any of my fellow classmates could struggle with their grades. I continued to get excellent grades in the second semester. Once again, I received first honors. I was very happy with my achievement.

One thing my homeroom teacher did during my first year in junior high was to teach us the capitals of all the 50 states of the Union. He had us study the states and capitals and learn how to spell each one. After that, he would have a competition between everyone in the class to see who was the best. I began studying with great enthusiasm.

The day finally came for the competition. He lined up one half of the class on one side of the room, with the other half on the other side. Then he began going back and forth with each group until we were down to ten. By the time we got down to the final ten, I was still there.

Again we went back and forth between the remaining ten until there were only two of us left. I was one of the two, along with Nancy Ann Palazzo. No matter how many states the teacher asked us to name the capital and to spell, Nancy and I always got it right. The

34

teacher realized he had a few exceptional students when it came to states and capitals so he decided to challenge the six other 7th-grade classes.

He picked the best ten in our class. He then told the teachers of the other classes to pick their top ten. They all did so and the competition began. First we challenged class 7-4. We went to their classroom and were lined up against the wall on one side, with the ten from the other class lining up on the other side. We then started. By the time the last student from the other 7th-grade class was gone, there were still three of us standing.

Next came class 7-3, then 7-6 and then 7-5. It was the same as with class 7-4; there were always three of us standing after the last student from the other class made an error.

The next class was 7-1. This was the big one for us. Class 7-1 had the top scholastic students in 7th grade. We had to go to their homeroom for the competition. It was the usual setup: the ten from our class on one side and the ten from their class on the other side. It went back and forth until there were two still standing on our side and six remaining on their side.

Normally, this would have looked like certain defeat. However, Nancy Ann Palazzo and I knew every state and capital, as well as knowing how to spell each. One by one, the students from the other side were eliminated when they made an error. Nancy and I kept answering every question correctly.

It finally came down to two against two. We now had to deal with the most difficult states and capitals. It went back and forth until they were down to one student. She was very good but she was no match for Nancy and me. She finally got a tough one and misspelled it. Nancy and I had done it. We had defeated the best of the best.

Nancy Ann Palazzo was the top student in our class scholastically. I was probably second to her. I had at that time of my life a very good memory. I did not have to study something very long to remember it. My toughest class was math. I cannot explain why. Somehow I just could not understand some of the principles of math. However, I still maintained a B average in math class.

The dystonia got worse in 7th grade. It is difficult to explain exactly how. I just knew it was more difficult to sit than ever before.

The pressure of the illness and the difficulty of getting around in the school started getting to me in the third semester. I missed a number of school days and my schoolwork faltered. When I got my report card for the third semester, I was shocked to discover that not only had I not made first honors, but also I did not make second honors either.

That was totally unacceptable to me. In anger, I told myself I would bring those grades up. I then focused completely on my schoolwork. Dystonia or no dystonia, I would not allow the illness to keep me from achieving honors in my schoolwork. I studied harder in school and at home.

When the fourth semester ended, my report card showed the fruits of my labor. I received the highest grades I had ever received in all of my years in school. I was within two grades of making straight A's. The principal had taken me aside earlier in the school year and told me that if my grades continued at their present level, I would be a prime candidate for a college scholarship. The thought of that was intriguing.

One of the things I discovered about myself in 7th grade was that I was a very good public speaker and reader. Whenever I was asked to read something, I always impressed my teachers with how well I read, as long as I did not have to stand and read something from a book, of course. In one class, my teacher labeled me as the best in the class after having everyone in the class recite the Preamble to the Constitution. I was very proud of that.

36

CHAPTER 6

While I did not get yelled at or humiliated like I did in my final year in Catholic school, there were still those adults who thought I was faking to get attention. At the age of 13, with my 14th birthday only a month away, I began to realize as I matured that faking my illness for the purpose of getting attention made no sense.

The doctors could think what they wanted to think. Drawing attention to myself by the way I walked and by the way I sometimes struggled to control my body while sitting only brought me the kind of attention I *did not* want. From a sheer logical standpoint, it simply did not make sense. Based on that, it was hard for me to understand how the doctors could have made such a diagnosis.

For some reason, the visits to the clinic had become few and far between. It was as if they had given up on me. Perhaps they were waiting to see if I would magically get better by being scolded and humiliated by the adults around me who were told I was faking.

When 7th grade ended, I began my first full summer living in West Warwick. I continued to hang out with Joe Andrewchow and Milton Eastman. There was a river nearby in the back of the two ball fields. Sometimes we played touch football with Johnny Zelski near that river. He was the pitcher for the West Warwick High School baseball team.

The dystonia affected me less playing football than baseball. Perhaps it was because at that time I could still run short distances. Since we were playing a contact sport, we really did not move in the same way as in baseball. One was expected to fall down sometimes when playing football.

One time Milton and I found an old sunken boat about a mile down the river from where the ball fields were located. We did not think anyone owned it so we bailed it out and got it afloat. We decided to take it upstream, closer to where we lived. We made some handmade paddles and began paddling. It was a lot of work but we managed to get there. We then hauled the boat to a pond about half a mile from the river where we had found it.

We eventually got a regular pair of oars to row it. Although I could row the boat, it was with great difficulty because my dystonia prevented me from being able to coordinate the necessary body movements. I felt bad because I thought people would think I was weak. I never actually told anyone how the dystonia made everything I attempted to do so much harder. Of course, at the time I had not yet been diagnosed with dystonia so what *could* I tell them?

When the summer ended, I prepared to begin 8th grade. I was then 14 years old. The dystonia continued to worsen and I experienced much more difficulty with both sitting and walking. Controlling my body was much harder than ever. Yet I continued refusing anybody else's help and struggled alone to get from one class to the next. However, it was beginning to wear on me.

I developed a fear of being called on to speak in front of the class, especially after the experiences during my last years in Catholic school. Eventually, I began fearing going to school. I was tired of struggling from class to class. I was tired of the humiliation the illness brought with it. I was tired of the constant battle within myself for muscle control.

My grades began to fall. I started missing more and more school. My first report card showed good grades but I did not make the honor roll. The second semester was even worse. I actually had a D in one of my subjects. That had never happened to me before.

In traveling from classroom to classroom, the struggle to get there was sometimes so great I would be out of breath by the time I got there. I can remember one occasion when I was on my way to class and one of my teachers stopped me and told me to take my time and stop worrying about being in class on time. He could see I was exhausted and breathing heavily.

Because my illness had worsened, a problem developed in finding transportation for me to get to school. They did not want me to take the bus because they thought it would be too difficult for me.

38

They decided I should be picked up at my house by a special van they used for disabled children.

The first day came for the van to pick me up at my house. When it arrived, I gathered my schoolbooks and lunch and entered the van. There was one other person in there, a girl about my age. I had never seen her before in school. She wore braces on her legs and used a wheelchair to get around. I felt bad for her. She seemed like such a nice person.

The dystonia had progressed to such a point that I was very uncomfortable riding in a car because it limited my movement so much. Such confined conditions lessened the ways I could counter the involuntary movements caused by dystonia. Under different conditions, I could make movements to the left or right to counter the muscle spasms. At home, I could get up from a chair and move around, then sit back down. In this special van, I could not do that.

In the van's confines, the only way I could keep my legs under control was by propping my feet against the floor near the back of the front seat. To control my arms, I had to grab the door handle or the window crank. I then had to strain my muscles to hold myself there. Having to do this all the time was both physically and emotionally draining, yet that was the only way I could travel in a vehicle. Obviously, I suffered a great deal because of that.

I saw the girl from the special van at a school party one time. I remember the sad look on her face as she watched all the other students dancing. Somehow, I sensed she was sad because she could not dance like they could. She looked so sweet sitting there. I could understand how she felt; we had a lot in common. That was the last time I ever saw her. I wish I had gone over to her at the party to keep her company. I did not like seeing people sad. Everyone should be nice to people like her.

The movements in my body reached a point where even tying my shoes became difficult. I would bend over to tie my shoes and my body would move to the right, away from the shoe. I had to force my muscles under control. I had to do that each day to overcome the debilitating effects of dystonia.

At that point, my parents started thinking about taking me to Children's Hospital in Boston, Massachusetts. I assume they were frustrated with seeing me getting worse and feeling so helpless to do anything about it. They never did take me there however. That was unfortunate because I likely would have been properly diagnosed sooner and my life would have been happier as a result.

By the end of the school year, I had made the honor roll only one time, in the third semester, and it was only second honors. Yet my grades, though lower than in 7th grade, were still slightly above average.

The summer came and Joseph Andrewchow and I went to Tiogue Lake. There we met a girl by the name of Elizabeth Mitchell. She was beautiful. Joe had a crush on her and so did I. Of course, I realized my chances of dating her were next to impossible because of my difficulties with dystonia. We spent a lot of time with her that summer, swimming in Tiogue Lake. She also invited us to her house and we had lemonade. We visited her numerous times during that summer.

Before the summer was over, my father bought a house in the Rice City section of Coventry. It was a big house with a barn and a huge yard, with apple trees and some pear trees. It was like living on a small farm. The house was way out in the country, a long way from the school we would attend. I liked the house and I was happy we had moved there.

CHAPTER 7

The school I was to attend, Coventry High School, was about six miles away from where we lived. I was now in 9th grade and 15 years old. In my first day at the new school, I reported to my homeroom. Coventry High School was a newer school than West Warwick Junior High School. Unlike West Warwick Junior High, Coventry High did not have a second floor.

I did pretty well while at Coventry High that year. My grades were still above average. However, I never again returned to the honor roll. While I would have liked to be on the honor roll, I knew my medical condition made that difficult.

A school bus picked up my brother Dale and me and took us to school. It was a very short walk to where we met the bus. That was helpful to me because by then walking had become quite difficult. The bus ride to school was quite long but because the bus was never full, there was always room to move around in my seat. That made it easier to control my body and offset the effects of dystonia. I pretty much stayed to myself on the bus. As the years passed while living with dystonia, I had instinctively developed my own mechanisms to survive with the illness.

High school brought some new experiences. One of them was a pep rally, when they bring all the students into the auditorium to root for the different sports teams. Pep rallies were a nice break in the day. I would have enjoyed them a lot more if not for the dystonia though. They packed us in the bleachers with no room to move. Because of the uncontrollable movements in my body from the dystonia, I was always uncomfortable. I did not want people to notice those involuntary movements but I was unable to move around to offset them. It was a very uncomfortable situation for me and caused me immense suffering.

I went to a number of basketball games during the school year. Our high school basketball team was not very good though. We also had a baseball team, a golf team and a track team. We did not have a football team at the time because the school system did not have the money to support it. I loved sports. Every time I went to a basketball game, I dreamed of someday being out there playing for Coventry High. I liked baseball too.

It was the same at Coventry High School as it was at West Warwick Junior High when it came to gym class. While I attended the gym class, they would not let me actually participate. I sat and watched as they worked out and played sports. It was tough because I wanted so much to be out there with them.

The first friend I made there was Wayne Dunbar. He lived in a farmhouse like ours about 200 feet from our home. There were big fields to the side and to the rear of his house. There was an old dirt road that ran in the back of his house that we used to walk to the fields located to the rear of his property.

Besides Wayne Dunbar, I also developed a friendship with Dennis Studly. While Wayne was my closest friend, Dennis Studly and I developed a mutual interest. He liked lifting weights and so did I. We set up a workout area in the room adjacent to the kitchen of my house, a room that we did not use and that was ideal for working out.

Dennis was quite strong. He lifted a lot more weight than I could. A lot of people did not think of Dennis as being that strong but having lifted with him, I knew he was. He once lifted 180 lbs. over his head. I thought that was very good for a person who weighed only 140 lbs.

I liked lifting weights. I got a subscription to a weightlifting magazine named *Strength and Health* and read it religiously. I followed the top Olympic weightlifters in the country through that magazine. At that time, the United States had the best weightlifting team in the world.

I believe the reason the dystonia did not affect my weightlifting that much was because I was using the muscles I could control, combined with the weight I was lifting, which offset some of the muscle spasms caused by the dystonia.

I also believe the level of concentration in lifting weights affects the brain in such a way as to compensate for dystonia. This appeared to be the case with me during that time.

Since I was very slender at the time, I could not compete with Dennis Studly very well when we lifted weights but I did what I could. At that time, I only weighed about 118 pounds. At 5'6," I was quite underweight.

I believe my slender frame was caused in part by the dystonia. From what I have read, dystonia appears to cause a person to be underweight in many cases because of the constant struggle to control body movements.

I continued to struggle to get from classroom to classroom but at that point I had almost three years of experience with that. Since 7th grade, I had been forced to deal with that problem so I was getting used to it. I finished 9th grade successfully and was promoted to 10th grade.

I cannot remember how long it had been since the last time I had visited Rhode Island Hospital's clinic. It seemed like well over a year. I think my parents had been frustrated by the lack of progress in dealing with my condition. The idea of taking me to Boston's Children's Hospital kept popping up but they never did take me there.

I really do not know if my parents still believed I was faking illness to get attention by that point. I doubt they did because they could see me suffering more and more as the illness got progressively worse.

While the progression of the dystonia was slow, it continued to worsen. Normal actions became increasingly difficult. Tying my shoes was one of them. Sitting comfortably in a chair was another.

Sitting in a chair is taken for granted by a normal person but when one has a movement disorder, it can become extremely uncomfortable. The right arm wants to go one way while the left leg wants to go another.

I turned 16 that summer. Wayne Dunbar and I hung around with a guy named Mark Capwell a lot. He had a car so we went with him to the populated area of Coventry. We would sometimes visit the Dairy Queen ice cream parlor near Tiogue Lake and buy an ice cream cone. Going to my favorite places in a car was a new experience for me. I started thinking about getting a driver's license.

CHAPTER 8

September rolled around and it was back to school. I was in 10th grade then. It was 1964 and the mini-skirt was in style. I was observing girls a lot more then. With mini-skirts so popular, I got to see a lot of legs. I can remember that when I was about eight or nine years old I used to wonder why any guy would be interested in girls. I did not feel that way any more.

My homeroom teacher that year was Mr. Ball. He taught mostly agricultural classes. My grades were pretty good. Beth Mitchell, whom I had met about two years before (as I mentioned earlier), attended my school and was on the cheerleading team. I still liked her. She was very popular in school. I liked seeing her at pep rallies.

One thing about me that I think I should mention here is that I have always had a great deal of ambition. I wanted good grades in school and I wanted to play sports. I also wanted to be an actor. I have never told anyone that before. Focusing on the achievement of goals such as these while having a disease like dystonia is very difficult and I knew that.

The thing about Dystonia Musculorum Deformans, also known as Generalized Dystonia, is that it affects almost every part of the body. Usually I had trouble controlling the right side of my body but there were also times when I would feel movements in my left arm or left leg as well. It could vary from day to day, hour to hour.

We had a cold winter that year. The pond below where Wayne Dunbar lived froze over. I had just gotten a new pair of ice skates. We all went down to the pond to skate. One would think a person with a movement disorder would not be able to ice skate. That is partially right. After putting my ice skates on, I went for my first skate. It amounted to about two feet. I got up and tried it again. That time, I traveled about four feet and fell. While the involuntary movements caused by the dystonia kept me from being a very good skater, at least I tried.

Before the winter ended, I went with my friends to another pond where a group of us decided to play some hockey. Of course, I wanted to play and my friends decided I should be the goalie. I tried my best but I kept falling in front of the goal. My friends were pretty smart. They knew I could not skate very well and that I fell a lot. They figured if I fell often enough, my falling would probably stop a lot of the goal shots from the other team. They were right. By the time the game was over, we had won with a score of 20 to 19 with me as goalie.

One of the elective classes I took that year in high school was typing. I honestly cannot remember why I took that class but I did. I guess it was something I wanted to learn. In my first class, I discovered something very discouraging. The teacher told us to be relaxed and keep our bodies straight in front of the typewriter. For me, that was a challenge I could not meet. My body would constantly shift to the right and no matter how hard I tried, I could not keep my hands on the keys. I could see my hands tremble in front of me as I struggled to keep my hands on the keys — dystonia at work.

I knew I would never be able to type because of the muscle spasms yet I stubbornly tried. I just could not control my muscles enough to stay on the keys. By the time the semester ended, I could type about 12 words a minute. I felt terrible. While it was the spasms of dystonia that kept me from typing, I still felt like a failure. I remember feeling a tremendous disappointment in failing that class. I thought about how fortunate my classmates were because they did not have to struggle every day to control their bodies, as I did.

Since we had not visited Rhode Island Hospital's clinic in such a long time, I still felt alone because nobody had ever said they did not believe what the doctors had said about my faking of illness. I was suffering but had only myself, and God, to turn to. I can remember one night, after failing miserably in typing class that day, I went to bed and asked God, "Why me? Why me?" Those words I had uttered many times before. I then lay back in my bed, with tears pouring down my face until I fell asleep.

46

Like any other kid, I wanted to learn how to drive. Wayne Dunbar's father had an old truck he let Wayne drive on the dirt road in back of their house. Wayne was a year younger than I was, but he already knew how to drive. He sometimes let me drive the truck. Little by little, I learned. Eventually, my father started teaching me how to drive also. Between my father's teaching and driving Wayne's father's truck, I reached a point where I felt I was ready to drive a car on the road alone.

In Rhode Island at that time one had to get a learner's permit before one could get a driver's license. Getting that permit required taking a driver training class to learn the rules of the road. The high school offered a class and I enrolled. There were about 25 of us there. We were given instruction books and I studied very hard. Getting a driver's license was a top priority for me.

The class lasted about a month and a half. On the day of the final exam, I was full of excitement. We began taking the test. I found it to be quite easy. I finished mine and took it up to the teacher. He graded them as they were brought to him. After the final one was handed in, we all waited nervously for the teacher to finish grading the last few tests. Finally he finished grading them and passed them back. I received an A. I could have passed the test with only a C but I wanted to be the best in anything I did in life and that was no exception. I was thrilled!

The permits were sent to us by mail. When I received mine, I was excited beyond description. Now I could drive legally on the road as long as a licensed adult was with me.

While I had received some training from driving Wayne's father's truck on the road behind his house, I still needed a little more experience on the road so I drove with my father. With the permit, we could go on the open road and that is what we did. After a couple of weeks of driving with my father, I felt I was ready for the test to get my driver's license. We made an appointment to take the test.

While I was confident in my mind that I could drive, the dystonia affected me a lot when I drove a car. I had difficulty moving my right leg to the brake. I also had difficulty getting to the clutch. I could do it but it took a lot of concentration and made driving more difficult for me than for the average person.

When the day to take the driver's license test came, I knew I would have to hide my medical problem, which might affect my driving, from the individual giving the test. I had not yet been diagnosed with dystonia.

When we got to the local branch of the Office of Motor Vehicles, I waited until I was called to take the test. I was tested on a vehicle with a clutch. It started off badly when I accidentally hit the brakes too hard and struggled to control my legs. Determined to get my license, I dug deep inside myself — as I had been forced to do so many times in the past — and focused my concentration on driving.

I dropped the car into first gear, braced my body against the seat and drove on, as I was instructed. I kept my mind focused on driving. I knew I had to hide my movement problem and I concentrated on that. It worked! I was able to hide the dystonia and passed the test easily. He only took off five points for the brake incident. I was issued a temporary license that day.

To the best of my memory, my parents never mentioned any concerns about my driving with such a medical problem. Of course, since I had been diagnosed a few years earlier as faking the illness, perhaps that was a factor in their thinking. They never talked to me about those things. That proved to be a benefit to me in a sense; with so many thinking I was faking the illness, I had a free hand to do things like driving without raising a red flag.

I did not have a car of my own so I used my parents' car whenever they let me. I can remember one particular occasion when they let me use the car. It was on a school day in the afternoon and I had not gone to school that day. I knew the time the school bus would be going down a certain road after school and I planned to wait for the bus, get in back of it and follow it just for fun.

The bus showed up on time and I proceeded to follow it. When it stopped to let students out, I would pull up to the back of the bus and wave to my friends. It was great being able to drive and I was showing off.

48

The truth was that I should not have been driving on the road because of my inability to control my body properly while driving a car. When I would pull up close to the bus, I would move my right foot to the brake pedal while holding down the clutch. I can remember looking down at my right leg and foot shaking badly from my struggle to keep my foot on the brake pedal. I also had trouble keeping my left foot on the clutch. It was not unusual for my foot to slip off the clutch while trying to change gears. However, I never told anyone about that because I was determined to drive.

The school year came to a close and I successfully passed into 11th grade. I continued doing well in my classes. While still not on the honor roll, my grades were still above average.

We visited my grandmother frequently. She lived in nearby West Warwick. I can remember a period of time when my father was out of a job and there was very little food in the house. We would go to my grandmother's house and she would always make sure we ate. When we left, she always filled a bag full of food for us to take home.

My grandmother came to this country from Italy when she was only 14 years old. She could speak only broken English. My grandfather, who could speak English well, had a drinking problem. He made his own wine with grapes he grew all around a little shack located on the property and kept it in a 50-gallon drum in the basement. He drank most of his wine himself.

My brother Dale hung around with my cousin Poncho and his brother Richard. I frequently tagged along when we visited them. I always had trouble keeping up with them because of the effects of the dystonia on my walking. They were not supposed to smoke but would go to one of the farthest locations on the property and smoke anyway whenever they could get cigarettes. I tried smoking a cigarette with them when I was about 12 but could not handle it and spit it out.

During one visit to my grandmother's house, I was tagging along with my brother Dale and my cousins when I discovered that if I bent over and placed my left hand on top of my left knee and my right hand on top of my right knee, I could walk without feeling the effects of the dystonia. Of course, I must have looked funny walking like that. Yet I was so excited because I felt almost normal. To be able to walk like that, without stumbling and falling, was a big thing to me. I mentioned it to my brother and my cousin but it did not mean much to them. That did not matter though; I had discovered something that might be helpful to me in getting around in the future.

Just after I started 11th grade, at 17, it was discovered that the previous owner of the house we bought had not paid the real estate taxes for a number of years. The bank foreclosed on the house and we were forced to move. I had to say goodbye to my friends.

We ended up renting a house on Knotty Oak Road in the same town so I did not have to change schools. It was a nice house with a decent backyard. There was a one-car garage attached to the house. The house was about a mile from the high school. That would prove to be a problem for me. The school rule on transportation was that anyone who lived within a mile had to walk to school.

My dystonia had progressed to a point where walking a mile to and from school would be very difficult. However, the school did not offer any assistance like a special bus so I was forced to walk. Sometimes my father gave me a ride to school but I still had to walk home.

At that particular time, I still did not know if everyone still thought I was faking my illness. No one talked to me about it and I had not been to Rhode Island Hospital's clinic in so long that I could not remember the last time I visited there.

The first day I tried walking home from school was quite an ordeal. I got out of school and started walking but my right leg kept turning in on me and I struggled to control it. It was a common pattern for my left foot to kick my right ankle when I attempted to take a step. While I had never actually seen what I looked like when walking, I was sure that at times it was a grotesque sight.

I made it to Knotty Oak Road from the school, which was about a tenth of a mile. From there it was a straight run to my house, just under a mile away. The walk from that point was brutal. I would take maybe half a dozen steps and fall down. Sometimes when I fell, my books went flying to the ground along with my lunchbox. I would gather my things back up and try to stabilize myself using the muscles I could control. Then once again I would concentrate on walking a

50

little farther. It was usually the same result: walk a few steps and fall again.

I noticed that along the side of the road there was a guardrail. I realized that if I could make it to the guardrail, I could use it for support. The guardrails were about 60 feet apart. That meant I had to travel 60 feet with no support. An extra effort had to be made to reach each guardrail.

I reached the first guardrail. Out of breath from the effort to get there, I sat down on the guardrail to rest. Once I had rested, I got up and again started my walk home. I made it to the end of the first guardrail and stopped to rest again. It took so much effort to walk even 60 feet that I ran out of breath. I then focused on the second guardrail.

To best describe my situation would be to compare it to a person dying of thirst in the desert who sees an oasis in the distance. Upon seeing the oasis, with his body almost drained of water, he makes a dramatic dash for the oasis in hopes of replenishing his body with water. That is a good analogy of how I felt; the guardrail was my oasis. The only difference was that I planned how to reach the next guardrail more carefully. I figured I would have to stop at least once, halfway to the next one. Since falling down had become a way of life for me, I did not worry about it.

After resting long enough, I got up from the guardrail and began my dash for the next one. I struggled and strained as one part of my body warred with the other. Sometimes the part I could control won the battle; other times the muscles I could not control took over. I stumbled almost to a crawl at the midway point. I stopped not to rest, but out of necessity. My body was all tangled up. I stooped down, which was a position that reduced the effects of the dystonia and gave me a chance to rest.

The next guardrail was only about 30 feet away. I decided to cheat that time. When I thought no one was looking, I started crawling to the next guardrail. I did not crawl long because I was afraid someone might see me and I would feel so embarrassed! I crawled for only about ten feet. I was much more confident when I was only 20 feet away from the guardrail.

I pulled myself back up off the ground and made what amounted to a dash toward the guardrail. I stumbled and felt myself falling. I bent down and placed my left hand on the ground to support myself so I would not fall again. Of course, by doing that I lost control of my schoolbooks, which I was carrying under my right arm. They slipped out of my grasp and fell to the ground.

After gathering up my schoolbooks, I struggled the remaining distance to the next guardrail, the same length as the previous one. With the guardrail as a support, it was relatively easy to move to the end of the railing. Then there were two more guardrails left and I used basically the same means of getting to them as I did with the first two.

The last guardrail brought me within sight of my house but I still had about 150 feet to go just to reach my front yard. Luckily for me, there was a chain-link fence in front of the yard of the house next to ours, about 30 or 40 feet from the end of the last guardrail. Tripping over myself, I struggled to the fence, falling once. For the second time, my books went flying out of my arms as I fell. Getting up again, I reached the fence and clung to it, pulling myself along until I reached the end of the fence.

At last, there was my front yard! It was about 20 feet from the fence. I struggled to it, once again bending down and using my left hand to brace myself so I would not fall. From there, it was a short distance to the house. Once I reached the front of the house, I used it for support to make it to the front door. I opened the front door, entered the house, threw my books on my bed, went into the living room and fell on the couch, totally exhausted. That was the scenario I went through each day when returning from school to my home.

There was another problem I encountered when walking home from school. I frequently saw people staring at me from their cars as I struggled homeward. I realized that was human nature but it was very humiliating to me. I am sure a lot of people felt compassion when they saw me like that but it only made me feel like a freak.

Unfortunately, it was also relatively common for people to pass by in cars and yell cruel things at me. Because I was totally deaf in my left ear, a lot of times I did not hear what they said so it did not bother me as much. That was one time the deafness in my left ear was beneficial.

I also realized that sometimes people in their houses or yards saw my odd way of walking and wondered what was wrong. Every time I saw people in their front yards, it made my trip home even more difficult because I then tried to hide from them my odd way of walking and my inability to walk straight.

Sometimes I just stayed sitting on the guardrail, hoping they would go back into their houses. Sometimes they eventually did go back inside and I then continued walking home. Sometimes I realized they were going to be outside a while so I was forced to continue on my way. I still tried to hide my problem but I am sure some of these people must have noticed anyway. No one ever talked to me. They just stared. I got angry with those people who stayed outside because their presence made my situation even more difficult.

The walk home was becoming unbearable for me as my condition worsened. After about two or three weeks of walking home like that, something happened that simply was too much for me to handle, combined with all the struggling I had already endured.

While walking home on that occasion, I noticed a woman watching me from outside the front door of her house. It really bothered me because I had not noticed her in time to stop before I reached her house. I realized that she had seen my odd way of walking and my struggling and it made me very angry and embarrassed.

What bothered me more was that she just kept staring at me. I stopped at the nearest guardrail as usual and noticed she was still staring. She finally went inside her house, closing the screen door behind her. However, she still stared at me through the screen door. That infuriated me even more and I decided that was the last time I would ever walk home along that particular route.

A few weeks prior to that day, I had gone for a walk in the woods in back of my house. I did not mind walking there because it was unlikely anyone would see me. I enjoyed the solitude the woods provided. While in the woods, I discovered a path that led to the back of my high school.

53

When the humiliating incident happened, I remembered that path through the woods and realized that if I walked home through there, the likelihood of not being seen by anyone would be virtually assured. I decided that the next day I would take that route through the woods when going home from school.

Nothing in the world is easy when one has an illness like dystonia and the walk home through the woods would prove to be no picnic. However, it would at least afford me the luxury of being free of prying eyes. That would remove at least one burden from my shoulders.

The entrance to the woods I chose was to the right rear of the back of the school. The distance to the woods from the school was about 100 feet. When school ended, I got together my books and lunchbox and left the school using a rear exit door. From there, I started walking toward the woods with the usual difficulty but finally made it to the woods and the path.

I had my books under my right arm and my lunchbox in my right hand. As I walked in the woods toward home, I used the trees for support. While leaning on one tree, I observed the location of the next available tree. Then with deep concentration I left the tree I was leaning on and tried to walk toward the next one. Oftentimes I did not make it and fell to the ground, with my lunchbox flying in one direction and my books flying in another. I then had to gather up my books and lunchbox and again head to the nearest tree.

In some ways, it was funny because as I bounced from one tree to the next it was as if I were a ball in a pinball machine. I did that all the way home. I fell anywhere from six to ten times, depending on my condition on any given day as I headed home. I had accepted falling down as a way of life for me and I got used to it, as stated earlier. What was important was that no one could see me, nor could anyone stare at me or laugh at me. It was part of my learning how to survive with dystonia.

Earlier in the book I described how I would kick my left ankle with my right foot while walking. At this point, I was doing this more often than in the past. There were occasions when I would kick the left ankle so frequently that I would develop a red spot on it. There were even a few times when I would break the skin, forming a bruise.

Sometimes while sitting in a chair, especially at school, the right foot would actually kick the left ankle when I went to move my right leg while it was under my desk. This too caused a bruise on my left ankle. In earlier years when I was in Catholic school, I tried bracing myself with my elbows while sitting at my desk and I wore holes in the elbows of my shirts. My elbows moved back and forth with very tiny movements on the desk. Over time, the friction of those movements wore out the fabric of the shirt.

The dystonia continued getting progressively worse. The discomfort while sitting was at times almost impossible to tolerate. I struggled to find some comfortable way of sitting. I simply could not overcome it, forcing me to suffer all the time. Psychologically, I was becoming more and more withdrawn. I had no one to turn to and still did not know if people still thought I was faking my illness to get attention. In my mind, I was alone in the world; like an animal, I had to fend for myself. While I did not cry every single night, I did cry myself to sleep on many occasions.

At this point of my life, 17 years old and in 11th grade, I had matured into a person who could reason. I knew there was something physically wrong with me and hoped somebody would do something about it soon. My parents said nothing to me. We never had discussions about my difficulties with walking.

I cannot remember exactly when we returned to Rhode Island Hospital's clinic but I know we returned while I was in 11th grade. I believe it was after Christmas. I cannot remember much about the visit other than that the attitude at the clinic seemed different than I had seen in the past. Nobody accused me of faking. They appeared to be taking me more seriously. They seemed more determined to find the problem.

As tough as school was on me because of the dystonia, it did have its rewards. The era of the mini-skirt continued and even though I had all those difficulties, I still enjoyed the sight of pretty girls at school. Also, the school finally found the money to support a football team so school pride was higher among the students than in the past.

55

I did okay in my studies but the dystonia was definitely affecting my schoolwork. It was becoming a distraction, interfering with my concentration and affecting the quality of work I did in each class. I started missing more and more days from school. I was becoming weary of struggling each day to get from class to class. I was so ashamed of the way I walked and how I must have looked, sitting in my seat at school with my body constantly moving in a grotesque fashion.

Also, I had problems in school with speaking in front of my classmates or even reading from a book at my desk. If a teacher in a class asked us to take turns reading from a book, I became petrified as my turn approached. When my turn came, I stumbled on the words as I read them, out of sheer fear. I felt as if everyone in the classroom was looking at me. By stumbling on the words, I felt even more humiliated. This was from a student who at one time had been one of the best readers in school. I was particularly afraid of speaking in front of the class.

There were times when I wanted to ask my teachers not to ask me to speak in front of the class. At one point, I was so scared in one class that when my turn came to speak I simply said, "I pass." The teacher in that class did not say anything to me about refusing like that and I did that again on occasion in a number of other classes.

I was so ashamed of the way my body moved that I could not handle attention being placed on me. It was a psychological problem that I would never totally overcome for the rest of my life. I was petrified like I had been in Catholic school. No one ever took me aside to talk about this problem.

I wish one of my teachers had taken the time to talk to me about some of these things. What I really needed at that time was the intervention of an adult. I was suffering deep social and psychological wounds no human being should ever have to suffer.

A lot of this problem came from what happened in Catholic school when I was scolded and humiliated in front of my classmates and accused of faking an illness to get attention. Also, movements from the dystonia while sitting down had increased and this, combined with the above, caused an increase of my fear. I withdrew within myself for what I perceived to be my own protection.

By the time I was 17, a simple haircut had become an embarrassing and difficult experience for me. I would always fear going because the dystonia bothered me while sitting in a barber's chair. Earlier I wrote how difficult it was getting an X-ray because I had no way of controlling my movements on the X-ray table. It was similar in the barber's chair.

The barber required me to be still and I was forced to struggle to control my body so the barber could cut my hair. I had to fight so hard to keep my body still. I suffered so much in that barber's chair, trying to keep my body from moving. I did many things to try to control the involuntary movements. I shifted my weight whenever the barber gave me an opportunity. I folded my legs in front of me, shifting from one position to another. This went on for many years, starting when I was about 11 and of course getting worse as I got older.

I often dreamed of playing basketball for the high school team. Every time we went to gym class, I sat down in the corner and watched everybody else playing basketball. In spite of the dystonia, I did play basketball when I was away from school. I was short so I was not really suited for it but I actually could shoot very well. I always sank about 60% of my shots from 15 feet out. I had a good eye and a soft touch. However, no one in my gym class was aware of that because I was not allowed to take gym.

One of the oddities of my dystonia was that I could offset the movements by doing certain things. When I played basketball, I had to bounce the ball and concentrate on going after the ball when it got away from me. This countered the effects of the dystonia. If I bounced a ball against the wall, it would bounce back toward me and I would have to move to a certain position to catch it instinctively. The key variable here was involuntary movement countered by voluntary movement and concentration.

In 11th grade, my grades were okay but I was still being affected by the dystonia in my scholastic activities. However, I was still slightly above average. The problem with the schoolwork was that the movements were affecting my concentration as noted earlier. Just sitting at a desk was so difficult to do with all the movements I experienced. My right leg would kick my left ankle, as mentioned earlier, but my left leg was also hard to control on occasion.

My right arm also seemed to have a mind of its own. If I tried to stretch both arms out at the same time, my body would twist to the right side. My left ankle would sometimes turn inward on me. The entire right leg would often move to the left when I raised it, with my ankle turned inward.

As the illness progressed, it took its toll on me emotionally. I never smiled and people always asked me why. I was of course unhappy because of my illness. I was becoming somewhat bitter. The suffering was so difficult to tolerate alone. I never spoke to anyone about the problem and avoided certain social situations where my illness might become noticeable.

Yet I continued to go to basketball games. I enjoyed them. I only wished that I could sit comfortably like everyone else. Elizabeth Mitchell, whom I mentioned earlier, was still on the cheerleading team. I still liked her. She was as pretty as ever. However, as the school year moved into spring, I was really getting fed up with the dystonia.

I realize today how critical my situation was at that time. I would be graduating from high school in less than a year and a half and I was still suffering from dystonia. I never thought about it then but when I finished high school, my normal projection would have been to go on to college or get a job.

My chance of getting a job was next to none. Consider how the dystonia affected me. Realistically, I could barely walk. That alone eliminated a lot of jobs. I could not sit comfortably in a chair even for short periods of time. I struggled to tie the laces on my shoes when I got dressed in the morning. I could no longer stand straight without support. In fact, I could not stand without support at all. It had gotten to the point in school where I could no longer study well because I had trouble holding a book steady enough to read. Who in the world would hire me?

In earlier years, I had more control than I had at this point. I rarely even read at all any more because I struggled so much trying to find a comfortable position. Dystonia had robbed me of so much; I was affected by the condition in virtually every aspect of my everyday life. It was only my strong desire to survive that got me through this point of my life.

That was about to change. In the first week of April while I was in 11th grade, my mother told me we had a doctor's appointment the following week. We were to see a doctor by the name of John Strom. Dr. Strom, a neurologist, was the doctor we had just missed seeing when we were late for the appointment at the clinic six years before, when I was 11 years old.

On the day of the appointment, I was surprised to find out we were not going to the clinic to see Dr. Strom. To my surprise, we were going right to his office. It was located a short distance from Rhode Island Hospital. We walked into his office and my mother went up to the receptionist to tell her we had arrived. After about a ten-minute wait, Dr. Strom came out and escorted us into his office. As soon as I saw him, I immediately recognized him as the doctor we had passed that day at the clinic when I was 11.

Why I recognized him after so long I do not know to this day. Perhaps it was because when he passed us as we were arriving and he was leaving, I thought maybe he was the doctor we were there to see.

I do not remember exactly what he had me do, but I remember him asking me to bend over and to walk. After I did both, he calmly told my mother and me that I had Dystonia Musculorum Deformans. I have no memory of my mother's reaction but I was ecstatic. After ten long and grueling years of suffering, my illness finally had a name. I felt vindicated! After all those years of being told I was faking, all the humiliation and all the tears I shed, yes indeed I had a real, honest-to-goodness illness with a name!

To think that I had just missed seeing this same doctor at the age of 11 was amazing. Had we gotten to the clinic just ten minutes or so earlier, I would have seen Dr. Strom that day and perhaps he would have diagnosed me with dystonia then. That would have meant I never would have been subjected to the humiliation of being improperly diagnosed as faking an illness. Furthermore, it would have led to treatment that would have improved me enough to be able to realize so many of my dreams.

The visit with Dr. Strom was very short. He filled out a couple of prescriptions for me to try to see if they would improve my dystonia. We picked up the medications he had prescribed, Artane and Valium, at the drugstore. I was to take each of them three times a day. Dr. Strom also set up an appointment for me to return to see him again in about two months.

It took ten years and about 20 or 30 different doctors to properly diagnose my condition. When I got home, I went out to tell everybody I had dystonia. To actually know what was wrong with me meant so much that it is hard to put it into words.

To have people telling you there is nothing wrong with you for six years, when deep down inside you know they are wrong, is an emotional burden beyond belief but it is especially so for a young child.

After about a month of taking the medications prescribed by Dr. Strom, there was no improvement. We went for our second appointment with him in the latter part of May. He changed my prescription to the Artane and added a drug called Kemadrin. I was to take three of each every day.

I began taking the medications the next day. During the first few days, Wednesday, Thursday and Friday, I noticed no improvement. On Saturday, I found myself feeling better and having a good day. On Sunday, I felt the same.

However, Monday was something else indeed. It was a totally normal day when I got into homeroom. I actually felt fairly good. When the bell rang to go to our first class, I was shocked. When I got up out of my chair something was different. I started walking out of the classroom and into the hall. As I started to walk to my next class, I was shocked again. I did not need the walls to make it to class. My body seemed straight and under my own control, unlike anything I had ever felt before. I was ecstatic!

When my first class ended, I got up and proceeded to my next class. Once again, I did not need the walls to make it. I also felt more

60

comfortable in my chair. By the end of the day, teachers were looking at me with rather confused looks on their faces. It was difficult for me to believe what I was feeling. After going downhill for about ten years, I was now, in my mind, cured. All that took place about a week before the end of the school year.

When school ended, I had a summer to explore my new life without the limiting effects of dystonia. I did a lot of things I could not do before or did not try to do because it was too difficult. I can remember wanting to walk all the time. Being able to walk almost normally meant so much to me after all those years of suffering.

We had just moved into a house on Johnson's Pond in Coventry. There were railroad tracks nearby and I walked the tracks every chance I had. I discovered a number of paths running away from the tracks and made a point of walking every one of them. It was like an adventure in the jungle as I traveled each different path, wondering where I would end up or what adventures I might experience. I could not understand why other people did not walk more often. My life with dystonia had taught me an appreciation for just being able to be reasonably normal.

Of course, I was not totally cured, as I would find out later on in my life. Yet I had improved so much that I felt cured. The fact that it happened so quickly was what was so amazing to me. I could drive a car much more comfortably than before.

I did visit the clinic one more time during that summer. We went to a doctor who was, to the best of my memory, an eye doctor. They checked my eyes for something I assumed had to do with my dystonia. Whatever they were looking for, they did not find it.

My second visit to Dr. Strom turned out to be my last visit to him. Dr. Strom assigned me to a doctor named Howard Triedman. I visited Dr. Triedman at the clinic for a few visits before we started visiting him at his regular office.

Because Dystonia Musculorum Deformans was so rare, I sensed I had become somewhat of a celebrity at the clinic. I was now treated with more respect. There was more serious attention. We had to pay for each visit but I could not help thinking maybe they should start paying me. I visited Dr. Triedman once before entering 12th grade. He asked me a few questions and gave me a renewal on my prescriptions.

I want to point out something here before I go any further. While I should have been diagnosed much sooner and never should have been diagnosed incorrectly, as I was six years earlier, the clinic should be commended for the help they provided for so many poor families over the years. All the patients who saw doctors at that clinic were poor and without the clinic, many would have received little or no treatment for their health problems.

I also would like to interject here that while in my mind I felt normal, I of course was not. The dystonia was still affecting me, but in a much smaller way. I am sure it would be fair to say that others who suffer from this disease would understand what I felt after improving so much so quickly. I think it would be fair to assume that many other young children that suffer an early onset of dystonia, as I did at the age of seven, have trouble distinguishing what is normal because of their young age. In later years, I would discover that the dystonia was indeed still there and would still affect me for the rest of my life.

The illustration on the next page is a good example of the kind of difficulties I had walking. The illustration shows how dystonia distorts the movements of the body. Note the curve in the left foot. Notice how the muscles in the back twist forcing the body into a bent over position sometimes pulling to the right sometimes to the left. This is very similar to the effects I experienced with early-onset dystonia when I was a little boy.

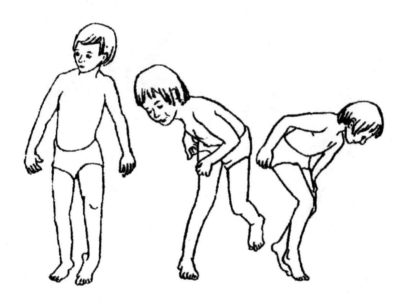

She barely noticed that when she ran, her left foot twisted.

Above is an illustration of a little girl with a very severe case of dystonia. As the disease progressed, her back arched, and finally her left leg was doubled so that her left foot was stuck against her buttocks. She could not be moved because of the intense spasm of all the muscles of her leg and back. Her right leg was stuck out like a ramrod, with her toes twisted and curled under the sole of her foot

CHAPTER 9

I was eager for the new school year to begin because I wanted to show everyone I was better. It began the first week of September. I took the bus to school because we were now living too far from the school to walk. The irony of that was that if we were still living on Knotty Oak Road, I would have enjoyed walking to school.

I had an entire summer of taking the medication prescribed for my dystonia. I was eager to see if I was even more improved than I had been in the final weeks of the previous school year.

On the first day of 12th grade, I found my walking back and forth to each class was quite normal. I never used the walls. My right leg never kicked my left ankle. While sitting, I felt so much more comfortable but it was the walking that really meant so much to me. I did not need anybody's help and I appeared to be walking normally, or at least close to it.

In gym class on the first day of school, I found myself still not allowed to participate. I told our gym coach I wanted to take the class. He seemed a little reluctant and told me he wanted to check with the school nurse to be sure it would be safe for me to do so. I was finally allowed to take gym by the third class of the year.

In that particular gym class, the coach took us outside. He wanted to test everyone in the 60-yard dash. I realized he was not going to ask me to try it so I told him I wanted to participate. He said okay with the same reluctant look on his face I had seen earlier. He probably thought I might embarrass myself.

I watched as one student after another took a turn while the coach timed each one. My turn finally came. I was determined to do well. He blew the whistle, telling me to go. I gave it everything I had. Upon finishing the race, I returned to the coach after the others had taken their turns.

He looked at me and said, "You know, Carmine, you did real well. In fact, you ran faster than a number of students." He was amazed I could run that fast. He never expected to see me beat any of my classmates. I, on the other hand, was disappointed because I expected to outrun at least half of the students in my gym class.

I mentioned earlier that I was a person with a lot of drive. I wanted to be the best in anything I did. So it should not be surprising that I decided to try out for the track team. One time at the end of the school day, I decided to run with some members of the track team and the football team.

The first thing they did was jogging. We all started together. It was to be a four-mile run. I discovered two things that day. One was that some football players could not run very long and never made it past two miles. The other was that I could not jog two miles, let alone four miles. I did beat a few of the other athletes. I actually beat a couple of the football players.

I discovered the next day that, at age 18, I was too old to be on the track team. That was a school rule and I understood the reasoning behind it. I also realized it took a lot of training to be on a track team. Even though I would have been satisfied just being on the team, I realized it was not going to happen.

The captain of the track team came over and told me he was impressed with my performance and urged me to continue. I appreciated his compliments but never did pursue it further. The reality was that the dystonia still affected me enough to make it more difficult for me to run than the average person. I still was not in total control of my body, nor would I ever be.

Even though I was not very tall, I played basketball when we had gym class. Even with the dystonia, I was a very good shot from 15 feet out at any position on the floor. However, I was not good on defense.

I can remember one particular gym class when we played basketball. As I took a shot from about 18 feet out, I could hear one of my team members groan, "No, no, don't shoot." The ball tipped the top of the rim and barely missed going in. I then heard the same person indicate surprise that I came so close to getting the ball in. That was a shot I had made many times in the past.

Something else happened that school year. I got a job as a sweeper in a company called Natco Products. They made tile flooring and other items related to household needs. The job was 30 hours a week and did not pay well. It was the first real job I had ever had. It was a burden with school and all but I was eager to make money to get a car and put gas in it. I bought a car, a 1961 Ford Galaxy. I could then drive to school.

In spite of the remarkable improvement in my dystonia, my grades stayed the same. The years of having the illness and not being properly diagnosed still haunted me and affected my schoolwork. That was very disappointing to me.

I still feared getting up in front of the class and speaking. I was still afraid to read from a book in a class because of what I had experienced in my earlier years. That fear would stay with me into my adulthood.

I was not popular in school before and that was not about to change. While I was pretty much normal by then, it was too late at that point to change my popularity. Had I been diagnosed correctly years earlier, I am sure things would have been different. I did not go to the senior ball. Of course, I would have liked to go but since the dystonia had been diagnosed only recently, I never had a chance to get to know any girls in my class that well.

By the end of the school year, I pretty much considered myself cured. We started preparations for our graduation. It was satisfying to know I would be graduating from high school. It would be my greatest achievement at that point of my life. However, there were no college plans. The dystonia had pretty much taken that away from me. While in high school, I had not taken college preparatory classes. My particular dystonia had progressed to a level that affected everything I did and I realized it affected my ability to concentrate on my studies as well. The stress of having to study much harder in more advanced classes would have been impossible with the progression level of the dystonia at that point of my life. My parents had never talked with me about college. Based on my dystonia, they may have thought college would have been too difficult.

I do not believe we had enough money for college anyway. My father handled money poorly and we suffered as a result of that.

We went through the usual graduation practice sessions. I can remember the first time I tried on my graduation gown and cap. It was so cool!

I felt so fortunate that they had properly diagnosed my illness and were able to all but cure it prior to my graduation. How difficult it would have been to sit outside with my classmates at our graduation ceremonies with the difficulties the dystonia would have created for me. I do not see how I would have been able to do it without embarrassing myself, hobbling along the way I would have. What if it was an especially bad day? What would I have done then? Thank God I did not have to worry about that.

The day of graduation finally came. We all put on our caps and gowns. I could hear the music before we started filing out to line up to receive our diplomas. The event was set up outside in front of the school. They had erected stands for us to stand on and sit on during the ceremonies.

As we paraded out, I could feel both tension and excitement. We all took our places in the stands. There were the usual speeches by the alumni. Then we had our student speakers. After the last speaker finished her speech, they began passing out the diplomas. They were done in alphabetical order. Since my last name started with a P, I had a long wait.

They finally started handing out diplomas with last names ending in P. I heard my name and I proceeded to go up front and receive my diploma. I did so standing straight and walking under my own control. I received my diploma with a smile on my face and returned to my place in the stands. After the last student received his diploma, we were dismissed and gave a loud yell!

CHAPTER 10
(The adult years)

With school done, it was the beginning of a new time in my life. To me, it was the post-dystonia era. I of course had to get a job. My first job after graduating from high school was in the textile industry. During those years after high school, I worked for many different textile companies.

We were still living on Johnson's Pond when I graduated from high school. I did not think about the dystonia very much any more. The medication was still working well. I was living a pretty normal life at that time. The dystonia was still affecting me to some degree but I did not let it interfere with trying to live a normal life.

I bought a motorcycle called a Bultaco when I was about 20 years old. It was a Spanish bike. It was classified as a street scrambler. The first time I tried riding it was at the motorcycle shop where I bought it. When I got on the motorcycle, I popped the clutch too quickly and the front of the bike popped up into the air, causing me to slide down the back of the motorcycle. The motorcycle then headed toward a gas station nearby and fell near a man pumping gas. Needless to say, I had the motorcycle shop drop the motorcycle at my house where I could practice learning how to ride it.

I discovered one thing when riding my motorcycle. The dystonia sometimes made riding the motorcycle uncomfortable. I often squirmed back and forth on the seat, trying to offset the movements from the dystonia. That fact made me realize I still experienced movements even though they were significantly reduced.

When I was 22 years old, I decided it was time for me to leave home and live on my own. I packed all my stuff and got an apartment on Adelaide Avenue in Providence, Rhode Island. The apartment was not much. It was one room with a tiny pantry. It had a tiny portable size refrigerator and a single-burner electric hotplate. There was a bathroom down the hall that I had to share with another person. The apartment cost me $12 a week. That was back in 1972.

Shortly after moving into my apartment, my car was broken into. There was not much damage. I was pretty sure who had done it because one of the guys who lived above me had been asking a lot of questions about my car the day before it was broken into. Not too long after that incident, someone broke into my apartment and stole my purple motorcycle jacket and some money. I also knew who that was but without proof, there was nothing I could do.

I had just gotten a new job in New Bedford, Massachusetts. It was a job extruding wire, which was the same kind of work I had previously done at Victor Electric in West Warwick, Rhode Island. It was about 45 miles, one way, to my job in New Bedford.

While living on Adelaide Avenue, I met an acquaintance and his sister Angelina at the local grocery store. After talking for a while, I learned that he and his sister were living about three streets down from me. After exchanging addresses with them, I left the grocery store and went home.

I eventually started dating Angelina. After dating for a number of years, we got married. Just as it was a rocky relationship before marriage, it was even worse afterward. The one good thing that came from it was the birth of my daughter, Catherine.

My ex-wife was not the best mother and eventually I was awarded physical custody of my daughter. She was four years old at the time. I was working on nuclear powered submarines in Groton, Connecticut when I was awarded custody.

It was a 50-mile ride from my house in Warwick, Rhode Island to my job, one way. That made caring for my daughter on my own very difficult. It was my plan to take Catherine to live with me full time when she entered 1st grade. Because she would be in school all day then, I would not need a babysitter for as long a period of time as I would if she were not in school. In the meantime, I would have my parents care for her.

In the early 1970s, I attended junior college. I had to attend on a part-time basis in the evenings because I was working full-time at that point. Going part-time, it took me five years to get my Associate Degree in Liberal Arts.

The house I was living in was a home I had purchased in August of 1978. It was a modest home with two bedrooms upstairs. I had gotten into an automobile accident, which was the other driver's fault, and I had received a small settlement. I wisely used it to buy the house.

Shortly after my daughter turned six, she moved in with me. She was very excited with the prospect of living with her father. I was also excited about her finally being with me.

I was able to get a girl up the road from us to baby-sit Cathy while I went to work. I enrolled Cathy in 1st grade. When the day came for her to start school, I took her to school on that first day myself and then went into work late.

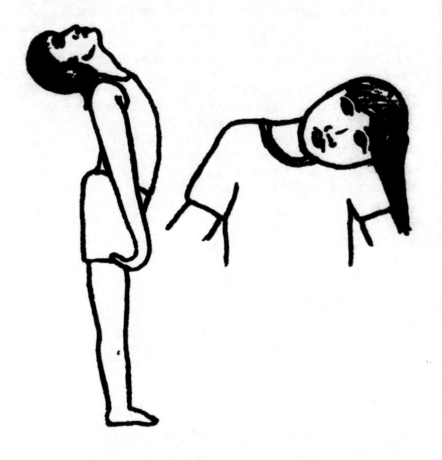

Above are two illustrations of Spasmodic Torticollis, (Cervical Dystonia). The first illustration is a dystonia posture called Retrocollis. The second illustration is a dystonia posture called Laterocollis. This form of dystonia is usually a late-onset dystonia. The positions in the illustrations are created by the involuntary contractions of the muscles caused by the dystonia.

CHAPTER 11

The job I had at Electric Boat in Groton, Connecticut was as a pipefitter. Becoming a pipefitter required extensive training. When I first applied for the job I was a little worried I might be rejected because of my dystonia. To my surprise, they hired me in spite of it. I was relieved because it was a good paying job. I started the job in August of 1978.

My oldest brother Dale also worked there. He helped me in getting the job at Electric Boat, a subsidiary of General Dynamics Corporation. General Dynamics Corporation built submarines, as well as planes and tanks, for the military.

This job meant a much better income than what I had in the past. I had applied to a number of companies over the years that paid well but was never hired. I suspect that my dystonia probably held me back. I tended to look for jobs that required moving around to help offset the dystonia. The pipefitting job offered exactly that.

The shipyard was huge. I was assigned an area referred to as the North Yard. There I got my first insight into being a pipefitter. I signed up for the apprenticeship program as soon as it was made available to me. Once accepted into the apprenticeship program, one got a significant raise and a promotion from 2nd Step Pipefitter to 6th Step Pipefitter. From there, one moved on to 3rd Class Pipefitter, then to 2nd Class and finally to 1st Class.

The apprentice program lasted three years and involved learning every aspect of submarine construction, with an emphasis on pipefitting. We learned how to read blueprints, install pipes, measure pipes and put bends in pipes, as well as how to correctly install valves and so forth. We even learned a little bit about other trades. While in the apprenticeship program, we went to work and then were bused to Electric Boat's apprenticeship training program facility. We attended classes there until lunchtime, then we were returned to the shipyard to work.

I had some trouble with understanding blueprints when I started working at Electric Boat. It was a definite weakness and I was determined to strengthen my blueprint reading. The apprenticeship program allowed me to overcome that weakness. In time, I actually became quite good at reading blueprints.

Working in the shipyard was not easy. During the winter months, we often had to work in the bitter cold. In the North Yard, the submarines we worked on were in the earlier stages of their construction, which meant they were not fully enclosed yet, so we worked on them under very cold conditions. I can remember when it was ten degrees on the boat, yet we were expected to perform our jobs in spite of the cold.

The way we dealt with the cold was to carefully use our coffee breaks to warm up. They wanted us to remain on the boat all the time and required a good reason for going back to the shop. Sometimes we had to make up a story to get back to the shop for a coffee break.

We worked in crews. Most crews had about 12 pipefitters, with one boss. Depending on the job, we either worked alone or two or more worked together on a specific job.

Prior to starting work at Electric Boat, we had received six weeks of training at a facility the company had that was a few miles from the shipyard. We were paid to take those six weeks of training; it was not much but it was enough to take care of us until we got accepted into the shipyard.

It took me a while to become good in my job. After working in the North Yard for about six months, I was sent to an area of the shipyard called the wet docks. At that part of the shipyard, we worked on submarines further along in their construction.

My brother Dale worked in that section as a pipefitter also. It was odd working in the same area as my brother. Dale had previously worked as a planner but had been laid off from that job a while back; he was waiting to be called back. Eventually, he would leave the wet dock and return to that planner job.

74

I had not noticed any particular problems with the dystonia. I never really thought about it much because my days were so busy, especially when my daughter came to live with me. I had to get up at 5:00 A.M. each weekday morning to prepare for work and to wait for the babysitter to arrive. Because of the time it took getting home, I did not return until after 5:00 P.M. It was like working a 12-hour day.

I commuted back and forth to Electric Boat by van with about ten other fellow workers. I had to drive six miles to get to the commuter parking lot where I would catch the van. We all had to pay its owner a certain fee each week to cover his expenses, including gas and upkeep of the van. I always tried to catch a little extra sleep during the ride to work, as well as during the ride home. It was about a 45-mile ride, one-way, from the commuter parking lot to the work site.

The van ride was sometimes difficult for me because on many occasions I experienced movement from the dystonia while sitting in the van. What made it so difficult was that we were frequently packed into the van like sardines. That made the trip to and from work uncomfortable. It was a more pronounced problem coming home because I was already so tired. I never told anyone about the dystonia because I did not want to draw attention to myself so I was forced to accept the situation and suffer alone. However, I was still much better than before, when I was still in school.

By the latter part of 1981, I graduated from the apprenticeship program. That automatically brought my classification up to 1st Class Pipefitter. The apprenticeship program had been very beneficial to my job. I overcame my biggest weakness, blueprint reading. They presented us with a diploma and an apprenticeship pin. It was gratifying to me to graduate from the apprenticeship program and to add that diploma to my high school diploma and my junior college degree.

The following summer I decided to take my daughter for a vacation to New Hampshire. It was a long ride. We visited an area of the state, near the famous White Mountains, where there were a number of tourist attractions. We visited a place called the Lost River, a very rocky area with water running through it. They had constructed

75

a boardwalk all along it, making it possible for people to get into the heart of the river area. There was a ladder located in one area, to use in getting down to a lower level where the water was.

They also had a western styled town, which we visited. Down the road from that attraction was a place called Santa's Village. My daughter Cathy enjoyed that immensely. Nearby there was a water slide in an area well known for its skiing during the winter. Cathy loved going down the water slide. They also had some other things to do there, one of which was a cable car that took visitors to the top of the mountain. This was of course used in the wintertime to take skiers up to the top of the ski slopes. In the summertime, however, it was used as a scenic ride.

We always stayed in a motel with a pool because Cathy always wanted to go swimming. She loved the water. Since I could not swim, I could only watch her.

While the trip was enjoyable for Cathy, it was not that great for me because the dystonia bothered me while I drove. It was not too bad on the way up to New Hampshire but it was very unpleasant driving back. I struggled to maintain control over the muscle spasms. I believe part of the problem was influenced by the stress of driving. It was particularly bad when I got lost at one point and kept driving anyway, determined to get back to where we needed to be. The more the stress intensified, the worse the spasms became and the tougher the driving got.

When that kind of thing happened, it was best simply to stop somewhere and rest if possible. Unfortunately, I could be a very stubborn person and that was when I started using poor judgment. I always felt guilty when that kind of thing happened because I did not want my daughter to suffer, as I did. God knows I did not want to try explaining my dystonia to her at her young age. However, the trip was pleasant for her overall and her happiness was always more important than mine.

I did not dwell on the dystonia when it affected me like it did on the vacation but it did annoy me when it interfered with my relationship with my daughter. Often on weekends, I wanted to rest from the week's work. I sat in the living room and watched television with my friend Roger Broulliard, who worked with me at Electric Boat. He was an inspector; his job was to inspect welding for quality.

My daughter often came over, wanting to sit on my lap. I let her but that made it difficult for me to move around to counter the dystonia's effects. I then became very uncomfortable and suffered badly. I sometimes pushed her away only because I did not want to endure the muscle spasms. It was not that I did not want her sitting on me, just that it was so uncomfortable for me. I always felt so guilty about that. At her young age, I knew she just wanted the security of being close to her father.

About two years after our vacation to New Hampshire, I decided to take Cathy on a vacation to Montreal, Canada. I arranged for us to make the trip by train. Amtrak had a train that left Springfield, Massachusetts and traveled all the way across the Canadian border to Montreal.

We were supposed to catch the train at 10:00 P.M. However, there was a big delay and the train was not going to arrive for at least three more hours. We were forced to wait. My daughter was ten years old at the time. We walked around the business district near the train station, trying to find something to do to kill time. That late at night, there was not much for a ten-year-old girl to do.

The train finally arrived at the station at around 3:00 A.M., five hours late. We got our luggage and carried it on the train. I searched for a good place to sit down. We took a seat near a window. The train ride was about 18 hours long. The train had a café car and Cathy was eager to visit that but I told her we probably should get some sleep first. Then we could enjoy the scenery in the morning light and eat after that.

Since she was little, she could stretch out on the seat and sleep fairly comfortably. It was not as comfortable for me but I was able to get about three hours of sleep. When I awoke, it was 6:25 A.M. Cathy was still asleep. I did not wake her until 7:30 A.M. By that time, it was daylight so we could look out the window and enjoy the scenery. Cathy was hungry so we went to the café car. Cathy looked so excited as we sat down to eat. She seemed to be taking all of this as a new adventure in her life.

I reflected on how hard life had been so far but looking at Cathy, I could not help thinking of how fortunate I was to have such a pretty little daughter and of how much she meant to me. I realized the magic a child could bring into one's life. For me, it was such a touching moment to have my daughter by my side and to go on that great adventure together.

The train ride to Montreal was very long. On the way up, I did experience discomfort while sitting for such a long trip but it was not too bad. I just did not want Cathy to know. I always thought it was important to hide any discomfort I felt from the dystonia because I did not want it to affect the enjoyment of what we were doing. I did that with everybody.

We reached the mountainous part of Vermont. It was beautiful! There was still some snow on the tops of the mountains, which made the scenery look even more stunning. Cathy appeared spellbound. We finally arrived in the city of Montreal. We got off at the train station and made our way to the street. It was then 7:00 P.M. I got a cab and told the driver the hotel where we were staying. When we arrived at the hotel, I got the key and we proceeded to our room.

The room was nice, as good as any in the States. We were both hungry so we went down the street to eat after we unpacked our luggage. We found a nice place to eat near the hotel. We then toured Montreal a little that night and toured it even more the following day, visiting many interesting sights.

We did a lot of walking. I was okay for most of the day but later in the afternoon, I began struggling to walk. Sometimes when I got tired, the dystonia began acting up more, causing my walking to become more difficult. When that happened, I usually could not enjoy what I was doing because of the increased concentration and effort needed to walk.

The following day, we boarded the train and began our long trip back home. For much of our Canada trip, we traveled during the night. It was surprisingly cold for that time of year. As the train returned to Springfield, Massachusetts, I noticed it was quite chilly on the train. I later learned the heat was not working. I asked for a

78

blanket but was told they did not have any on board for the passengers.

Cathy was cold so I gave her my jacket, which left me freezing. I cuddled up as best I could to stay warm, but to no avail. On top of that, my dystonia acted up so I was not very comfortable for the entire trip back home. Yet it was still a good trip because my daughter got to see another country. To me, that was most important. As long as she had a good time, that was all that mattered to me.

The above illustration shows two views of a 49-year-old man suffering from Spasmodic Torticollis (Cervical Dystonia). The left view shows a retrocollic posture caused by marked spasms of the neck. The right view shows the hyperextension of his neck has been reversed by the use of Spinal Cord Stimulation. In some cases the position in the illustration can be fixed causing the individual to be unable to move the neck into a normal posture.

CHAPTER 12

My job as a trained pipefitter was interesting. It involved many different aspects of pipefitting. Sometimes I worked on copper pipe and sometimes I worked on nickel copper pipe. At other times, I installed a valve. Submarines had miles and miles of piping in them. I was one of the smallest pipefitters in the shipyard. A lot of the piping was located in very tight areas a big person could not fit in. Some piping was located in small tanks where maneuverability was difficult for a large person so I was constantly assigned to many of those tight areas to work because I could fit in much more easily.

Often I had to crawl along the hull of the submarine in back of the diesel engine, behind the crew's mess and in many other very tight areas. The hull was divided into frames. I often had to travel across a dozen or more frames to get to where the work had to be done. That made pipefitting a very physical job at times.

I relished working in the tight areas because it was a challenge and because the bigger guys could not fit, meaning they could not do a job I could do. Crawling into those tight areas involved twisting my body in many different ways to fit into a spot. That was physically demanding.

Over time, constantly doing that led to a lot of wear and tear on my body. I always thought of myself as being indestructible. However, it was perhaps inevitable for me to sustain an injury at some point during my employment at Electric Boat.

When I was at Electric Boat, I spent a lot of time working in the torpedo room. Most people can identify with the torpedo room because it is referred to in so many movies. It was not a difficult area to work in and a lot of the work was easier to get at than in some other areas of the submarine.

In November of 1985, I was installing a group of piping to the overhead area while I stood on a ladder. As I stepped down with the pipe after taking some measurements, I felt a pain in my back. I reported to the yard hospital to have it checked out.

I was placed on light duty for a while. Light duty was when a person suffered what appeared to be a minor injury and was assigned to easier work until the injury had sufficient time to heal. After doing light duty for about two weeks, my back had not recovered so I went to see a chiropractor for treatment. It was determined I had suffered an injury to the lower back that would require missing at least two weeks of work to allow for full recovery.

I ended up missing three weeks before I went back to work. Then I was okay until April of 1986 when I suffered much the same injury, though a little worse, and ended up missing almost six months of work.

More tests were performed and it was discovered I had disk degeneration in the lower back in the areas called L4, L5 and S1. That was determined through a CAT scan. Missing two weeks of work was one thing, but missing six months was difficult. I went back to work in October, still experiencing some pain but hoping to work through the pain as a baseball player might do when suffering an injury.

My boss was very good about it. He did not ask me to do heavy work and tried to find less strenuous work for me. However, I could not sit on the submarine and watch a member of my crew working and being in need of assistance without helping him.

My boss saw this and always said, "Here is a guy with an injury trying to help when I have others in the crew who are healthy trying to avoid working."

In the early part of 1987, I went to the yard hospital for therapy whenever the pain flared up. I wanted to get through the injury and return to the work I had been doing before. The treatment was in the building next to the yard hospital. They had a therapist there equipped with the usual items found in a therapist's office. My therapy consisted of heat and massage of the lower back. The therapy kept me going and afforded me some relief.

During that period, I developed some problems getting back and forth to the submarine. It was not serious but began to be noticeable. On one particular occasion as I returned to the shop with my tools, I

82

saw my boss motion to me by lifting his shoulder up and down. As it turned out, he had noticed my right shoulder rising and falling while I walked.

I had not really noticed it myself but after he pointed it out, I made a point of looking for it. Sure enough, my shoulder moved up and down while I walked. That was the first evidence that the back injury was having an effect on the dystonia.

I have since realized I was experiencing a dystonia called Spasmodic Torticollis. Considering that I was experiencing muscle spasms from the back injury and still feeling some movement from the Generalized Dystonia, it made sense that I would have some difficulty walking even with all the medication I was taking.

The pain continued but I kept working. During the spring, I began losing weight. By the summer, my weight dropped from 140 pounds to 122 pounds. It was then July of 1987 and I was exhausted. Moving around the shipyard became more and more difficult yet I wanted so badly to continue working. My fellow workers were like family to me. I did not want to leave them.

However, I finally suffered an increase in back pain on July 15th; I realized I would have to leave work again because of it. Tired and frustrated, I went back out on Worker's Compensation, not realizing I would never return to the shipyard again.

Earlier in the year, while I was still seeing a chiropractor, arrangements were made for me to have a Metal Resonance Imaging (MRI) scan done. An MRI is considered better than a CAT scan because of its ability to pick up more detail than the classic CAT scan. The MRI was to be performed at a facility in Massachusetts.

I arrived at the facility for the MRI scan at about 9:00 A.M. After filling out the customary paperwork, I was taken into the room where the MRI machine was located. I was instructed to lie on top of the table that protruded from the machine. I was told the table would slide inside of the machine, with me lying on the table. Once inside, it was very important for me to remain completely still during the scanning process. I was told it would take about 45 minutes for the MRI scan to be completed.

The table was moved into the MRI scan machine. I was again instructed to stay still. That of course was very difficult because of the dystonia but I tried very hard to remain immobile. We got through part of the imaging process okay but as time passed it became much more difficult for me not to move. The 45 minutes started feeling like hours to me.

After a period of about 35 minutes, I was told they needed to try again to get certain images that did not come out correctly because of my movements. I told the person doing the imaging of the dystonia and how it made it so difficult for me to stay still. However, I told him I would do my best not to move again.

We tried again to get the remaining images. I gave it everything I had to keep from moving but it just was not possible. As much as I had improved with the medication, I still had difficult periods like I experienced at that very moment. Without the ability to offset the movements, I could not hold still the length of time necessary for those final scans.

Although the person doing the scanning could see I had tried my best to keep still, he gave up on the final scans. The other scans came out all right so at least we had those to work with. They proved to be enough for the doctor to interpret the level of the problem in my back.

In that situation, where being completely still was necessary, I did the following to try to keep still. When I was first put into the MRI machine I waited for the technician to tell me when he was starting the scan. At that point, I took a deep breath, closed my eyes and concentrated on being still. When I felt a movement coming, I instinctively flexed an opposing muscle to counter the movement. If I felt my left leg about to move, I concentrated on that leg and if necessary I flexed the muscles in that leg to the point of being totally fixed. That took effort and expended much energy. When I felt my lower back attempting to twist, I immediately flexed the back muscles I could control to try to offset that twisting movement. I could flex the muscle performing the involuntary movement to the point of being rigid. The problem was that I could only do that for a short time. Then I had to resort to something else to keep my body still.

Concentration was the other element in the process of keeping my body under control. I had to continue thinking ahead of each approaching muscle spasm as I felt it beginning. I also carefully figured out when the short periods in the scanning process occurred so I could rest my body long enough before we started again.

With the test completed, I returned to the waiting area for the results. After about 20 minutes, the technician came out with them. I was informed that because of some movement during the MRI scan they were unable to get better results. However, the scan revealed bulging at the locations of L4, L5 and S1 in the lower lumbar region of the lower back. That bore out the results found a year earlier from a CAT scan. We then had viable evidence of the source of the back problem.

That raised serious questions in my mind regarding my dystonia. Back injuries cause muscle spasms in the lower back. While significantly controlled by medication, my dystonia caused muscle spasms in the lower back and elsewhere. What possible effect was the back injury having on my dystonia?

Out of work and now haunted by the thought that my career might be over, I was torn as to what to do next. My daughter would be okay because I was receiving Unemployment Compensation. What would I, or could I, do? It had become apparent the dystonia was being affected by the back injury and there was no real cure for the injury. The back problem had now grown into a chronic problem with chronic pain. Would the dystonia reappear in full force?

I had been receiving treatment for my back problem from a neurosurgeon named Eugene Russo. He was a doctor who had been recommended to me by a friend, Norman Demers, whom I had met shortly after I graduated from high school. Norman also had a back problem and had been out of work for a long period of time.

In my first appointment with Dr. Russo, I found him to be very attentive to what I had to say. I explained to him about my history with dystonia. He gave me a prescription for the pain related to my back injury and discussed a treatment involving intravenously fed Robaxin with me. He explained I would be in the hospital about four days for that procedure. My friend Norman had mentioned this treatment to me earlier because he had received it in the past and had experienced pain relief for several months afterward.

I agreed to try this treatment, which would be done at St. Joseph's Hospital in Providence, Rhode Island. I arrived in the morning on the date of my admission to the hospital. There was a battery of tests I went through before being officially admitted. About two hours passed before I was finally taken to my hospital room.

The hospital room held two patients. I met my roommate when I arrived. He had just received back surgery and was in the process of recovery. I unpacked the small suitcase I brought with me.

The nurse came in and introduced herself as my nurse for the day until the next shift came in. She instructed me to put on the hospital gown, the normal attire worn after admission into a hospital. At that point, it was 11:30 A.M.

My roommate told me they would serve lunch around 12:15 P.M. While talking with him, I learned he had just had his second surgery on his back. The first had not gone well. He explained he had high hopes the second surgery would turn out much better than the first.

I did not receive my first injection of Robaxin until after supper, around 6:30 P.M. They utilized a plastic bag containing the Robaxin drug in liquid form, which hung from a metal pole with wheels on the bottom so I could walk around with it. The metal pole allowed me to go to the bathroom or just walk around to get some exercise.

To continuously inject the Robaxin, they inserted a long needle into a vein, usually on top of the hand. With the needle properly placed in the vein, they then inserted the line leading from the bag to a small fitting attached to the needle inserted in the arm.

With that done, they then regulated the flow by using a small valve located about two feet from where the line was connected to the hand. They then opened the valve until they saw the desired amount of liquid Robaxin dripping from the valve into the vein. That was the same procedure used to feed a person intravenously.

It did not take long for me to start feeling the effects of the drug. While it tended to induce drowsiness, I found it to be very relaxing. It took about 12 hours for the bag to run out of the drug.

When the drug ran out, the needle remained in the vein as the insert in the line leading from the bag containing the drug was removed. At that point, a small needle with a vial of a substance used to clean out the insertion point was injected into the needle and vein to avoid possible infection.

On the following day, another bag of the liquid Robaxin would be attached to the fitting and the same procedure would be repeated. During my four-day stay in the hospital, I received a total of four bags of the liquid Robaxin.

Patients with significant back injuries dominated the ward where I stayed. I met one patient who had already had three surgeries and was still in pain. I remember him well because he had expressed to me his frustrations and his feeling of letting his family down because of his back injury. He was near tears while he spoke. I encouraged him as best I could by telling him to be patient and that things would get better. I found similar stories throughout that ward during my four days in the hospital.

The Robaxin seemed to work well. I noticed some relief for a few months after receiving the treatment. I returned to the same hospital again for Robaxin treatment two more times. I could not say for sure, but my dystonia seemed to improve with the treatment. My walking seemed better and even sitting felt a little more comfortable. Perhaps the drug relaxed the muscles enough to have a positive affect on my dystonia.

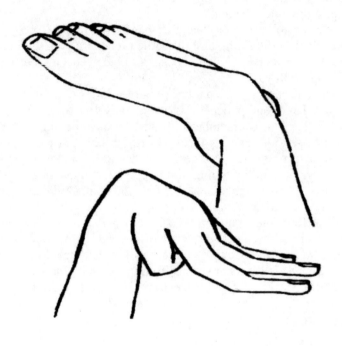

The above illustration shows a deformed hand and foot. Note how the wrist is severely flexed in a fixed position with the thumb fixed against the palm of the hand. The ankle is curved inward making walking difficult or impossible depending on the severity of the spasm. This is common in, Generalized Dystonia

CHAPTER 13

It was the latter part of 1987. After realizing the back injury was affecting my pre-existing dystonia, I went to the local library to see if they might have a book on dystonia. They had one book, and only one book, on the disease. It was titled **The Victim Is Always the Same** and was written by Dr. Irving Cooper. Dr. Cooper was a neurosurgeon who had an office at St. Barnabus Hospital in New York City. Dr. Cooper had become somewhat famous for a radical brain surgery for the relief of patients with advanced symptoms of the condition called Dystonia Musculorum Deformans, with which I had been diagnosed.

The story involves two different girls with severe early onset dystonia. The main focus, however, is on a girl named Janet, who had such a serious case of dystonia that she had body parts locked into fixed positions.

This is common in severe cases of dystonia. Fortunately, I have never gotten to that point. However, had I not found medication to relieve the majority of my dystonia symptoms, I have no idea what might have happened to me two or three years later. I highly recommend this book.

Except for the fixed positions, I could identify well with the different things Janet had gone through as described in the book. In particular was the failure to be properly diagnosed. It is amazing to think that any doctor could not see the obvious physical disability in the case of Janet!

After reading the book, I noted the location of the hospital. I got the address and sent a letter to Dr. Cooper at St. Barnabus Hospital in New York City. In my letter, I explained my dystonia and my recent back troubles. I asked if there were any new treatments for dystonia sufferers. I was not aware at the time that Dr. Cooper had passed away. I believe I sent the letter around December of 1987. I got a response in about two weeks.

With the response to my letter, I received a package and a letter from a doctor named Joseph Waltz. I was informed of the passing of Dr. Cooper. In the package was detailed information about a device called a Spinal Cord Stimulator. In Dr. Waltz's letter, he mentioned the device and indicated he believed he could help me.

In the package of information was also an explanation of the different forms of illnesses for which it could be used. Besides dystonia, it mentioned Spasmodic Torticollis, a particular form of dystonia, and cerebral palsy. It also could be used for people with spinal cord injuries. The materials referred to success rates in the utilization of the Spinal Cord Stimulator in the treatment of the illnesses listed above.

After receiving this information, I took it with me on my next visit to Dr. Russo. He told me that St. Joseph's Hospital had a doctor who had installed this device before. Since I was about to enter the hospital for more Robaxin treatment, it was arranged that during my stay I would be given a consultation with that doctor. With that understanding, I left the material with Dr. Russo so he could pass it on to this other doctor.

Upon entering the hospital, the doctor visited me on my second day there. Out of respect for the privacy of this doctor, I will refer to him as Dr. John. We left the hospital room to speak in privacy in the waiting area nearby.

Dr. John informed me he had reviewed the material I had supplied and that he would be willing to perform the surgery. He made no guarantees about the success. He told me the device would be placed in a certain location in the cervical area. After being installed, it would be evaluated using one specific setting. He further stated that if I did not respond to that particular setting, I would not improve from the use of the device. That seemed to conflict with the material I had received. However, since Dr. John was a member of the hospital staff at St. Joseph's Hospital, it would be easier to have him perform the surgery than to travel to New York City to have the surgery done there.

90

I made an appointment to visit Dr. John at his office. At the appointment, Dr. John discussed the matter further and gave me a preliminary examination to evaluate my health and to examine the level of my dystonia. His conclusion was that I had Spasmodic Torticollis.

At the time, I knew my underlying problem was dystonia. In looking back on my history with dystonia, at a younger age I did not appear to have symptoms connected with Spasmodic Torticollis. They were more related to Dystonia Musculorum Deformans, Generalized Dystonia. Yet a while later, I realized that I did indeed suffer from Spasmodic Torticollis as well.

In May of 1988, I was admitted into St. Joseph's Hospital for the surgery. After settling into my hospital room, Dr. John visited me later in the day and explained the preparation and surgery to take place the following day. I had undergone surgery before for a broken jaw I had suffered several years earlier. That helped prepare me for the upcoming surgery.

On the following morning, the nurse made sure I was up early to make last minute preparations for the surgery, set for 8:00 A.M. They came up for me at 7:30 A.M. I was transferred from my bed to a wheeled bed used to take people down to the floor where the operating room was located. Once there, I was prepped for the surgery. An intravenous tube was inserted in my hand. I would be under general anesthesia, which meant I would not be awake during the surgery.

I was wheeled into the operating room for the surgery. A receiver was installed on the upper left-hand side of my back. An incision was made at that location large enough to set the receiver in place. A wire lead was installed by guiding it into place under the skin in the cervical area of the neck to a specific location. The wire had four electrodes attached to it. Four wires were attached to the receiving unit; these were also attached to the four electrodes installed in the cervical area. After installation of the Spinal Cord Stimulator device was completed, the incision was closed. I spent time in the recovery room and was then returned to my hospital room. I woke up in my hospital room a short time later, feeling fairly normal except for the incision.

Dr. John did not come to my hospital room until much later in the afternoon. He brought with him what looked like a suitcase, which he used to test the receiving device. I was in possession of the transmitter. Dr. John, with the assistance of a nurse, hooked me up to the device that looked like a suitcase and placed what is called an antenna on the area where the receiving unit was installed. The antenna was connected to the external transmitter.

He then turned the unit on. I immediately felt a jolt of electricity. I jerked, as if I had just stuck my finger into an empty electrical socket! Seeing the expression on my face, the nurse was horrified, as was Dr. John. The doctor did not seem to know what was going on. As for me, all I knew was that I wanted the doctor to stop everything, which he did.

He then tried it once again but that time he built up the level of stimulation gradually until I could feel it. After concluding I was at the appropriate level of stimulation, Dr. John left the transmitter at that level. He instructed me that they would now wait a few days to see if there was any relief from the dystonia.

After a few days in the hospital, I had not experienced any relief. Dr. John decided the Spinal Cord Stimulator was not going to work. After discussing this with me, a date was set up to surgically remove the stimulator two days later. A day after that surgery, I was released from the hospital.

I later realized Dr. John had not done the procedure correctly, according to the information supplied to me by Dr. Waltz's office. The company Dr. Waltz used had not made the device Dr. John had installed. I spent seven days in the hospital and made two visits to the operating room, only to have the wrong device installed and then removed. I had nothing to show for it all but a couple of scars on my upper back. Dr. John should have researched both companies before installing the device.

I decided to set up an appointment with Dr. Waltz at St. Barnabus Hospital in New York City. After about a month had elapsed, I contacted St. Barnabus Hospital and Dr. Waltz's office to consider having the surgery there. I had not traveled to New York City in a long time and looked forward to seeing the city again.

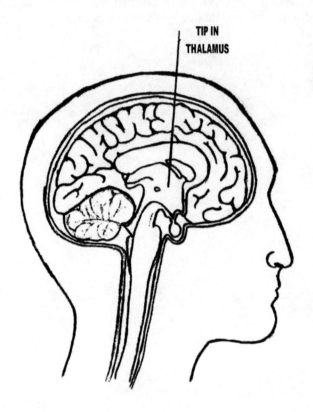

**TIP IN
THALAMUS**

The above illustration shows the location of the tip of the probe in thalamic surgery. This area of the brain is called the Thalamus. It is the area of the brain that controls movement.

CHAPTER 14

I first traveled to New York City to visit Dr. Waltz at St. Barnabus Hospital in August of 1988. St. Barnabus Hospital was located in the South Bronx section of New York City. While I had the choice of taking a cab or taking the subway, I decided to take the subway. After getting directions on which subway trains to take, I finally reached 3rd Avenue, where St. Barnabus Hospital was located.

After getting off the subway, I had to get a transfer to take the bus at 149th Street to 183rd. It took a while but I finally figured out where to board the bus for the trip to St. Barnabus Hospital. The bus arrived and I got on. It took about half an hour to finally get to St. Barnabus Hospital at 183rd Street and 3rd Avenue.

After searching around a while, I was able to locate the building occupied by Dr. Waltz. I went up to the second floor to Dr. Waltz's office. I checked in at the desk and then went to the waiting room. There were several newspaper articles hanging on the wall referring to the successes Dr. Waltz had achieved with the Spinal Cord Stimulator in the treatment of cerebral palsy, as well as dystonia and Spasmodic Torticollis. Many of them were quite remarkable.

I was finally called into Dr. Waltz's office, where he discussed the Spinal Cord Stimulator device with me. I told him about the failed surgery at the hands of Dr. John. He understood my disappointment.

After a brief discussion, he sent me to another office that I believe was located on the first floor, although it might have been in the basement. In that office, a medical assistant took film of me sitting in a chair. It would be used in the future to compare for any improvement accomplished with the use of the Spinal Cord Stimulator. With that done, I left to return home to Rhode Island, where I was staying with relatives.

I had to wait to get approval from Worker's Compensation to cover the cost of the surgery. It was approved in about three weeks.

From that point, a date for the surgery was set in September, only three months after the surgery performed by Dr. John.

With plans set for the surgery at St. Barnabus Hospital, I purchased tickets to take the train from Providence, Rhode Island to New York City. Upon my arrival in New York City, I headed for the subway and followed the same travel scenario I used the first time I visited Dr. Waltz.

When I arrived at St. Barnabus Hospital, I was assigned a room in the building right next to the building where Dr. Waltz had his office. I cannot remember its name. It was very convenient being able to stay on the hospital premises before the planned surgery, which I was to have the next morning.

To recover from the surgery, I would return to this same building and room. The surgery would be performed on an outpatient basis, which meant I would not stay overnight in the hospital.

That first day, I also got to meet Wayne Andreesen, Dr. Waltz's technologist. He would be assisting Dr. Waltz; he would monitor the testing process after the installation of the Spinal Cord Stimulator. I found Wayne to be very friendly and a very likable person.

The next morning, I reported to the main hospital building to be prepared for the surgery. I would be placed under local anesthesia this time. It was necessary for me to be awake during the surgery so I could communicate with the doctor as to whether or not I could feel the stimulation from the device after it was installed.

With the intravenous line set up, I was wheeled into the operating room. Once in there, I was prepared for the surgery by being placed with my back exposed while lying on my stomach. My face rested in a little holder to provide comfort during the surgery. I could feel layer after layer of sheets being placed on top of me.

At that point, Dr. Waltz told me he would begin sticking a needle in the areas to be cut to numb them so I would feel no pain. Slowly, the doctor began inserting the needle in one spot after another. Not being fond of needles, it was very difficult to just lie still while he stuck me again and again. It hurt at first but once the area started becoming numb, I could not feel the needle any more. Then he went to another area and started again. All the while, he kept talking to me.

96

He was very good at helping me tolerate his procedure. What made it particularly difficult for me was the presence of movements during the surgery. These movements were particularly troublesome because of the length of the surgery.

When Dr. Waltz had finished injecting me with the local anesthesia, he started telling me what he was going to do each and every time he was about to do it. He would make incisions in three different locations. He told me when he was making his first incision. He constantly asked if I felt any pain. It seemed like an eternity by the time he finished the third and last incision.

He then had to begin the process of setting the electrode lead in the proper location in the cervical area. To do this, he used a device to guide the lead with the electrodes into place in the cervical area. A fluoroscope was used to monitor the lead as it was guided into the appropriate position. At one point, he must have hit something with the guide because it really hurt. Other than that, I did not feel anything as he guided the lead into position.

It was tough going through this because I had to fight off the effects of the dystonia during the surgery. I had to rely on Dr. Waltz talking to me throughout the ordeal. The nurse and the others in the operating room were also comforting.

With the lead in place, Dr. Waltz then devoted his attention to installing the receiving unit. This was a small round metal piece with four electrodes attached evenly on four sides. I could almost feel the doctor installing the receiver. The receiver unit was connected to the lead in the cervical area containing the four electrodes with four wires.

With everything in its proper place, the time for testing the Spinal Cord Stimulator arrived. The external antenna, which was taped over the spot where the receiver was installed, was placed into position. The external antenna was then attached to the transmitter. When the antenna was installed over the receiver, the transmitter was then adjusted to an adequate level of stimulation that was tolerable to me.

Once the test began, I could feel the effects of the stimulation. Dr. Waltz tried a few different settings and I was asked to indicate what I felt, which I did each time. The stimulator was working properly and the ordeal was finally over.

After leaving the recovery room, I returned to Dr. Waltz's office. There I met with him and with Wayne. Wayne went through the different settings we would be testing. There were 18 different settings used initially in the process of finding the best one for the treatment of my dystonia.

A flowchart was used to keep track of the level of improvement I experienced, if any, with a specific setting. Each of the first 18 settings was examined over a 24-hour period. The effectiveness was analyzed and entered into the flowchart as better, same or worse in comparison with the previous setting. One section of the flowchart sheet was titled Observations. In that section, I briefly described what I experienced during the testing of each individual setting. The 18 settings consisted of 12 settings using only two of the four electrodes, while the remaining six settings used all four electrodes.

When this process was completed, the best of the 18 settings tested were selected and then examined again over a 48-hour period, in the same fashion as in the original 18 settings. The same process was used in these tests as was used in selecting the best of the original 18 settings.

Once this testing was completed, the best of these settings were identified. At this point of the testing process, I usually had five or six settings left to test. The remaining few settings were analyzed over another 48-hour period until the best setting was found. Once that process was completed, the next step was finding the best frequency level.

The frequency can be adjusted in increments of 10 Hz. The range of frequency can be from as low as 20 Hz to as high as 1,500 Hz. It is rare for anyone to use anything near a frequency of 1,500 Hz. In my case, the highest frequency we did try was 1,500 Hz. We started at 100 Hz and moved up by 100 Hz until we reached 1,500. 100 Hz was usually the starting point for frequency testing and that was the frequency I used most of the time. In my case, we found some effectiveness at 200 Hz and also at 500 Hz. Frequency adjustments were always done in consultation with Wayne, Dr. Waltz's technologist.

After a few more days at St. Barnabus Hospital, I packed up and left with my new Spinal Cord Stimulator. I could not help feeling rather unique. I had this medical implant installed internally in my body, which was operated by an external transmitter and an external antenna taped to the area where the receiving unit was installed. The transmitter was attached to my belt using a belt clip.

I took a train to New York City; then I took another train to get back to where I was staying in Rhode Island. I liked traveling by train. I enjoyed the scenery as the train chugged along, taking me home. Any time I wanted a cup of coffee or a sandwich, all I had to do was go to the café car and get what I wanted. The train ride was comfortable even though I had undergone surgery only four days earlier. The three incision areas were a little uncomfortable when I lay back but by being careful when moving around I felt okay.

During the testing period, there was improvement at times, followed by no improvement. I discovered that sometimes a setting would be good for a while but then it would seem to lose its effectiveness. This proved to be a pattern, making it very difficult to find the best setting and frequency. Often I had to change the setting because it started losing its effectiveness.

Overall, the Spinal Cord Stimulator provided some relief but I do not consider it significant. The medications I take are much more effective than the stimulator. However, I cannot help wondering what would have happened had I had the opportunity to install the Spinal Cord Stimulator when I was diagnosed with dystonia way back at the age of 18 instead of at 41, my age at that time.

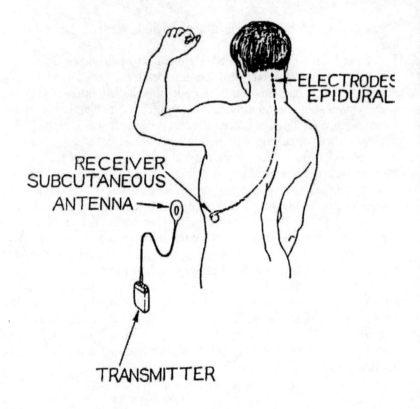

ELECTRODES
EPIDURAL

RECEIVER
SUBCUTANEOUS
ANTENNA

TRANSMITTER

The above illustration shows the entire Spinal Cord Stimulation System including the exterior transmitter and antenna as well as the internal parts consisting of the receiving unit and the electrodes. For dystonia the electrode lead is installed in the cervical area. For lower back pain the electrode lead would be installed in the lower lumbar region of the back. The number of electrodes in the lead varies from four to sixteen.

CHAPTER 15

In August of 1989, I visited Florida because I was considering moving there. I had been told the weather in Florida was good for people with back problems. I viewed a number of homes through a real estate agency in Florida. I learned about them from a booth they had at a mall in Rhode Island. I found a house I was interested in and returned to Rhode Island.

By September, I decided to buy that particular house. I made an offer, which was accepted by the contractor. The sale was handled through the mail. The closing for the house was finalized in the last week of September. I planned to move down to the house in the last week of October.

To my dismay, my daughter, now 15, refused to go with me. My father showed an interest in renting the house I owned in Rhode Island. That surprised me and may have been the reason my daughter would not come with me to Florida. I decided to rent my house to my father, with his understanding that my daughter would live with him. He was happy with that. Paul, my second to youngest brother, would also live with my father. With all that settled, I prepared to make my move to Florida alone.

I regret to this day that I did not make my daughter come to Florida with me. In the 12 years I have lived here, I have always missed seeing her each morning.

Moving to Florida was an exciting trip. I traveled through states I had never seen before. I reached Washington, D.C. by about 5:00 P.M. I was traveling down Interstate 95, which went straight through to Florida. I did not stop at a motel until about 9:00 P.M. I was in North Carolina at that time. I got up bright and early the next morning. I wanted to reach my new home that day. I left the motel at about 7:00 A.M. My destination was Inverness, Florida. I arrived there at 4:30 P.M. My new home was located off a street called South

Apopka. I drove up South Apopka until I finally found the street my home was on.

In January of 1990, I joined an organization called The Citrus County Property Owners Organization. They were a group of residents that formed for the purpose of protecting the interests of the citizens of Citrus County relating to their homes and taxes. They met once a month. This group gave me the opportunity to be involved in the community. When I attended the February meeting, they elected me to be their secretary. I felt honored. Later I found out the secretary's position was one no one else wanted.

I still experienced pain in my lower back. The dystonia was still a problem but it was under control using medication and the Spinal Cord Stimulator. I am sure the dystonia was contributing to the pain but I could not really be sure how much.

Because dystonia causes many patients to walk in an abnormal way, it tends to affect a person's skeletal structure. Knowing that, I visited a chiropractor to get checked out during one period in 1991. During the examination, it was discovered that I had a tilted sacrum. The sacrum is located in the lower central part of the back. The chiropractor was able to straighten out the sacrum through the use of chiropractic treatment in about four visits. I did notice a reduction in pain after that treatment.

Besides the sacrum, another problem area was the cervical area. During my adult years after the age of 40, I occasionally experienced tightness in the back of my head that was very uncomfortable. It sometimes lasted two weeks or more. While it did not cause a headache, it caused something similar to that, more of an annoyance than anything else. I have always believed it was caused by the dystonia. I believe it was a symptom related to Spasmodic Torticollis.

When I was younger, I had more trouble with the lower body. In later years, it seemed to change more to the upper body with lesser effect in the lower body. It is difficult to explain because dystonia began affecting me at the early age of seven so I have never been able to know what it was like to be normal.

102

By 1991, The Cites County Property Owners Organization changed its name to The Citrus County Taxpayers Association. I was elected to the position of president.

As the president, I became more involved in making presentations before the local government. We voted on ideas our organization had developed at our meetings and I conveyed those ideas to the Board of County Commissioners. The Board of County Commissioners consisted of five members elected to office to run the county. I also presided over our organization's Board of Directors meetings. I liked being involved in the community in my own small way.

In 1991, the Spinal Cord Stimulator suffered an internal defect. It was not unusual for internal problems to develop. The receiving unit was one of the more common parts to develop problems. Sometimes it would be an electrode in the cervical area. Whenever it was an internal problem, it required surgery. I had to be cut open for the problem to be located and repaired.

I had to make the trip to New York from Florida. I stayed with my family in Rhode Island while I was up there. From Rhode Island, I took the train to New York City. When I got to New York City, I took the subway to the hospital just as I had in 1988 when I had the Spinal Cord Stimulator installed.

When I arrived at Dr. Waltz's office, I met with Wayne again, the technologist for the Spinal Cord Stimulator. I was told before I arrived that I would be staying in somebody's home near the hospital. Wayne told me how to get to that residence, referred to as Bunny's. After finishing my meeting with him, I left for the room provided for me at Bunny's.

The room turned out to be directly across the street from the backside of the hospital. Bunny, presumably the owner of the house, met me at the door. She was very friendly. She showed me to the room I would be using. It was fine for me, clean and comfortable. I unpacked my things, then left to get a bite to eat.

I had never visited the area around the vicinity of St. Barnabus Hospital. It represented a varied cross-section of different nationalities and people, as did all of New York City. During my

103

walk around the area, I was amazed when I came across the Bronx Zoo. Then I thought, 'Of course! Where else would you expect to find the Bronx Zoo but in the Bronx?' It was a mile or two from the hospital. I bought a sandwich on my way back to Bunny's and ate it in my room.

Later I went down to the first floor, where we were allowed to use the living room to watch television. While I was there, a cab arrived with some people from Argentina. They had a child with a severe medical problem but I did not know if it was dystonia. I had never met anyone else with dystonia. However, I knew Dr. Waltz treated such patients from all over the world.

I retired to my room to prepare for my surgery the next day. It was kind of lonely to go for surgery in a place so far from home. I could not even imagine what it was like to come all the way from Argentina with a sick child to a country with a different language.

Morning arrived and I prepared myself for the walk over to the hospital. Once there, I proceeded to the area where one was prepped for surgery, adjacent to the operating room. There they installed an intravenous line in a vein on my hand. They also gave me something to relax me.

Then I was wheeled into the operating room and was prepared in the same manner as when I went through the original installation of the device in 1988. They called this current procedure a revision because they had to find out what was not working internally.

Everything was the same as in 1988 except that I handled the needles for the local anesthesia very well. It was starting to become routine for me. It was discovered that the receiver was not operating properly; they also found that the lead in the cervical area was not working. They proceeded to replace those items and the operation was over after they checked with me to see if I felt the stimulation.

After spending a short time in the recovery area, I dressed in my street clothes and walked to Dr. Waltz's office to see Wayne and Dr. Waltz. With Wayne, I went over the settings test again to find the best settings for me. After that, I saw Dr. Waltz briefly and then went back to where I was staying at Bunny's. I rested a while; then suppertime arrived. Bunny invited me down for dinner.

Around 8:00 P.M., I went back up to my room. I was in bed by 10:00 P.M. It was always difficult going to bed after that surgery because the doctor had to make incisions in three different places to remove the old internal parts and replace them with the new ones. When lying on my back, the staples the doctor used to close the incisions dug into my back a little and caused some discomfort. I found myself constantly moving from one position to another. That night the dystonia bothered me too, making it very difficult to find a comfortable position for the dystonia and for the surgery incisions on my back.

I left New York City two days later and returned to Rhode Island. I then returned to my home in Florida after having the staples removed. Within a couple weeks, my incisions had healed to a point near normal.

I would have three more revisions after the one in 1991; the last one would occur in February of 2002

Before I left New York, I got a prescription for massage therapy. I began getting a massage once every other week and found it relieved some of the back pain. It also appeared to help me somewhat with the dystonia but it took many months of massage to feel improvement for that particular problem.

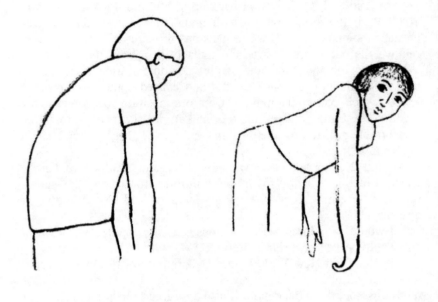

The first figure in the illustration above has Axial Dystonia. Notice how the muscles in the back force the shoulders to rise towards the head. Axial Dystonia affects trunk and neck muscles. It can also cause speech and swallowing difficulty. The second figure has dystonia that affects control of the muscles in the lower back, and trunk. Also note the difficulty in controlling the left arm as well as the right arm. Control problems could also include the legs and feet. Because of the multitude of control problems of different parts of the body this would commonly be referred to as Generalized Dystonia.

106

CHAPTER 16

A problem occurred with the knob that controlled the amplitude on the Spinal Cord Stimulator's transmitter. The amplitude controlled the output of voltage from the transmitter, which operated on a nine-volt battery. If the amplitude knob brushed up against something, it would sometimes turn up to the highest level, which caused my wrist to bend inward and also forced my hands to curl up and my fingers to become fixed together. When that happened, I had a difficult time reaching the transmitter to lower the amplitude setting.

That happened to me on one occasion in a parking lot and I could not reach the transmitter. I had to yell for help from someone in the parking lot to turn down the amplitude knob for me. Fortunately, there was a person nearby who came to my assistance. I had the individual take the transmitter off of my belt clip and reduce the amps.

In 1996, this happened twice and caused very serious, dangerous circumstances for me.

In the first incident, I was in the parking lot of a shopping center near my home. I had just stepped out of a drugstore. It was raining very hard and I ran to my car, quickly opened the door and slid inside. As I slid into the car, the amplitude knob on the stimulator brushed against the seat, forcing it up to its highest position. This immediately caused my body to contort into a fixed position. I could bend my back but my legs were immobile, my arms were very difficult to move and my elbows were fixed to my sides.

I knew I had to reach the transmitter to turn it down and immediately tried moving my hands toward it. I could not quite reach the transmitter and even if I did, I could not use my hands because the fingers on both hands were locked and my wrists were bent upward. I was literally curled up into a ball, almost totally immobile.

I realized I was in trouble. The window was rolled up, making it difficult to yell for help. I began sweating profusely as I futilely attempted to reach the transmitter. I began to yell, hoping someone would help me.

I noticed an elderly couple parking their car just across from mine. I yelled for help directly at them and finally caught their attention. Unfortunately, they apparently did not want to get involved and ignored me. Perhaps they thought I was dangerous. A few minutes passed and a van driven by a young woman parked nearby. I yelled at her. She apparently saw me but started her van up again and moved farther away from where I was parked.

I hoped a police officer would come along. I knew time was running out for me. It got hotter and hotter in the car. I decided I had to get out of the mess on my own. I thought it might be possible to open the door. I reached for the doorknob but after repeated tries I realized I could not get my hands under the door handle far enough to open it.

Then a thought occurred to me. If I could reach the area of my back where the antenna was taped to the implanted receiving unit and pull the antenna loose, I would be all right. The problem was how to get under my shirt. There was only one possibility. I took my left hand and hooked it under my shirt on the left side, then took my right hand and did the same thing on the right side. With both hands positioned, I began pulling my shirt apart by breaking off one button after another, finally reaching the bottom of my shirt.

The antenna was taped to the left side of my back, about halfway up. All I could do was to try getting my left hand to the location of the antenna and hope I could break the tape away. I put my left hand in the area and moved it around the taped area. To my surprise, it worked! I was able to pull the tape away enough to reduce the amplitude; I then pulled the antenna off completely.

I fell back in my seat as an overwhelming sense of relief washed over me. After 15 minutes of struggling, I was finally free! The force that had bent my hands inward put so much pressure on my wrists that they were sore for a few days.

108

In the second incident, only two weeks after the incident described above, I was getting ready for bed. While lying in bed, I noticed I was not feeling any stimulation from the stimulator device. I increased the amps to see if that would help but still I did not feel anything. I increased it even higher but still felt no stimulation. Occasionally, the antenna became defective or developed a short inside and if I jiggled the wire around, sometimes that restored power. I tried that but had no luck.

I turned the amplitude knob close to its highest position. Still I felt nothing so I felt confident in turning it to the very highest level. Big mistake! It suddenly clicked on and my body immediately contorted into a ball while lying on top of the bed.

I could not believe I was so foolish as to put myself in the same situation I had been in only two weeks earlier. However, this situation was even worse because I was alone in the house late at night with no way to contact anyone for help. I thought I was doomed for sure.

I had to figure out how to get out of my predicament. Lying on the bed was bad because the mattress's flexibility made moving around difficult. I realized I needed to get off the bed somehow. The only possibility was to roll off.

I began rocking back and forth on the bed until I gained enough momentum to roll off the edge of the bed and onto the floor. Once on the floor, I had to figure out how to get to the transmitter. I tried repeatedly to reach it but could not. I did not know for sure if I could survive if I were forced to wait until the battery in the transmitter died. I knew that would take at least 12 hours. There seemed no way out of the situation.

There was no way I could reach the antenna lead near where the antenna was taped to the receiver. I tried not to panic so I could think clearly. I found I could reach the wire leading out of the transmitter by twisting and rolling my body to the left. Yet since most of my body was in a fixed position, I could not do anything with the wire. I stopped to consider the situation and a thought occurred to me. What if I could get the wire in my mouth? If so, I might be able to bite through the wire.

I twisted my body as much as I could to get closer to the wire. A combination of twisting toward it and shifting my body around eventually brought the wire close enough for me to grab it with my mouth. Desperate and scared, I began chewing on it. Within a very short time, I chewed through the wire and my body immediately went back to its normal position. Boy, was I relieved!

Today, Advanced Neuromodulation Systems (ANS), the manufacturer of the Spinal Cord Stimulator, has developed a new transmitter that is digitally controlled, making it impossible for that problem ever to happen again. I now have one of those models.

CHAPTER 17

I was still president of the Citrus County Taxpayers Association in 1996 when something happened that would have a great impact on my life. The organization had made arrangements to have a political forum in the third week of June. I would be the moderator at the forum.

On the afternoon of the event, I went to the room to be used for the forum to make sure it would be properly set up. As I was moving a chair, I suddenly felt a sharp pain in my lower back. Every time I bent a certain way, I got a sharp pain. The pain stayed with me as the day wore on and I knew it would still be around when we had the forum. Yet since it did not bother me if I avoided bending a certain way, I felt confident it would not interfere with my duties in conducting the forum.

As my officers showed up for the forum, I told them so they would take on extra responsibilities and I would not have to move around as much. The meeting went well. Each candidate was given ample time to speak and the forum was a big success.

The sharp pain continued but it did start to improve within a week. I thought it improved enough for me to go fishing on my boat, which I did. That was a mistake. Every time I leaned to the right or left, I felt a sharp pain. On a boat while fishing, I had to do a lot of leaning. I ended up coming back early from my fishing trip.

By the Fourth of July, I was still experiencing sharp pain so I decided it was time to visit the local hospital's emergency room. Because it was the Fourth of July holiday, there were not many people at the hospital and the emergency room was almost empty.

I was called in and was placed in a room to wait for the doctor. After a bit of a wait, a nurse showed up and proceeded to ask me questions regarding the back pain. She then informed me I would be getting X-rays taken. I went to the X-ray room, had the X-rays done and returned to the emergency room to wait for the results.

A doctor showed up shortly and asked me only one question. He wanted to know which side of my back hurt so he would know which side of the X-rays to look at. I told him it was mostly the left side. After he left, I could not help wondering why he would ask such a question. Would he look at one side of the X-rays more than he would look at the other side?

The doctor came back in a few minutes and told me nothing about the X-rays. He told me he would get me a list of doctors I could consider seeing. He left abruptly before I could ask him any questions. He could not have been with me longer than 30 seconds.

After he left, a nurse came in and made me take some medication. She told me not to drive while taking that medication because it could put me to sleep. Since I drove to the hospital alone, I was glad I only lived about a mile away so I could get home before the medication put me to sleep. The nurse then gave me a sheet of paper with instructions telling me to take it easy for three days. She then told me I could leave.

As I dressed to leave the hospital, I realized I had not yet gotten a list of doctors to consult further on my condition as the doctor had promised. As I passed the front desk, I saw the doctor with his feet up on the counter, talking to another person who worked there. This doctor had only 30 seconds to consult with me but had plenty of time to shoot the breeze with another hospital employee! I never did get that list of doctors he promised. I left no better off than when I arrived.

Three days after that, on a Sunday afternoon, I went to sit down on my couch in my living room. As my body hit the couch, I felt a sharp pain worse than any I had ever felt in my life! I sat there motionless for about five minutes before I tried to move. Within an hour or so, I was in much more pain than before. If I stood long, I developed even more pain. I was forced to lie down to alleviate it at all. Eventually, I discovered my leg was numb around the shinbone and left ankle.

In the latter part of the evening, I decided to call the emergency room at the local hospital for advice. They advised me not to come down because they were busy. I thought that was a strange thing to say to someone in my condition. Yet since this was the same hospital I had visited on July 4th, it probably was good advice.

By late evening, I knew I was in very bad shape and that this injury was serious. I had a lot of pain medication at my disposal so I thought maybe it could get me through the night. I called the emergency room again and asked their opinion. They agreed. I took a little more pain medication than usual. While I did not sleep much that night, I did survive till morning.

The pain was getting worse. I found I had to lie flat on the floor to avoid the worst of the pain. When I got the newspaper that morning, I had to read it while lying on the floor. I called the emergency room again. This time they gave me the names of orthopedic doctors in the area to contact about my back injury. I wrote down each doctor's name while lying on the floor in my living room.

They gave me about six or seven names. I called each one but their offices all told me they did not treat back injuries. Since at that time no neurosurgeons practiced where I lived, I had no one else to contact.

The back pain forced me to spend the entire day on the floor. I made a TV dinner and was forced to eat it while lying on the floor. The pain did improve slightly by evening. I went to bed early after taking more pain medication. By the next day, the pain was somewhat better. I could stand for longer periods.

In the afternoon, I thought of trying to go to another hospital, 22 miles away, for assistance. I called first and was told to come on down. However, the instant I stepped into the car, the pain was so intense I realized I could not make it to the hospital. Later that afternoon, I tried walking up the road only to have my left leg freeze up after walking only 50 feet. I felt numbness around my left shinbone, my left knee and my left ankle. My left leg buckled whenever I turned a certain way, sometimes causing me to fall down.

113

I knew I really needed to visit a doctor with some knowledge of back injuries so I made an appointment to see a doctor in Tampa. I could not get an appointment until the latter part of July but I scheduled it anyway. My back had improved to the point that I felt I would be all right until then.

The medical facility was about 80 miles from my house. I arrived for my appointment on time and was seen by a doctor who was an assistant to the doctor in the office. He was being trained prior to getting his own practice. He was a pleasant doctor and I felt very comfortable with him. He did a very thorough examination. He concluded I had a severely herniated disk in the area of L3, L4 that probably needed surgical intervention.

The doctor he assisted came into the room at that point to evaluate the diagnosis. That particular doctor did some work in the area of movement disorders and that was one of the reasons I had chosen him. It was decided I needed to have a myelogram done and I was scheduled to have it done a week later at a local hospital.

I arrived a week later for the myelogram. I had to stay over a half day in the hospital. A myelogram was scheduled over an MRI because the implanted parts of the Spinal Cord Stimulator system were made of metal and an MRI could not be performed on anyone with metal in the body.

A myelogram is one of the prime tools used to locate defects in the disks of the spine when someone suffers a back injury. It consists of shooting a dye into the spinal area and then performing an X-ray of the region with the dye, which exposes damage to spinal disks. It is one of the most effective methods in determining the severity of back injuries. However, a myelogram is not one of the more pleasant experiences a person can have. It requires the use of a large needle to inject the dye. In some people, the after-affects can be very significant. Headaches and stomachaches sometimes occur from this procedure.

I was brought down into the area where the myelogram was to be performed. An area of my lower back was prepared for injection of the dye. After injecting the dye, an X-ray was taken. While I was still on the X-ray table, the results were brought over to me. The X-ray technician pointed out to me that I had sustained a huge herniation, with the disk projecting deep into the spinal canal.

This of course was bad news. It made surgery a very big possibility. After getting home from the hospital, I developed a headache and a stomachache like nothing I had ever experienced before. That lasted six long days.

I have never felt as sick as I was during that six-day period in my entire life. If you can avoid a myelogram, by all means do so.

Having back surgery is never an easy decision to make. It is especially difficult if you suffer from the form of dystonia I have.

I knew my back twists occurred in the lower back area where the surgery would be performed. A thought occurred to me. What happened if the surgery was a failure and I developed lower back spasms even worse than what I presently experienced?

Since Dr. Waltz's office was located in New York City, it made sense for me to see a doctor in Florida to evaluate the situation with my back. I made an appointment with a neurosurgeon located in the same building where I saw the doctor who had authorized the myelogram. (I had seen the neurosurgeon once before by mistake on a matter relating to something else.) I made an appointment to see him the following week.

My first meeting with this new doctor was brief. We discussed the possibility of surgery. He was against it for some reason that he never explained to me. He sent a report to the doctor's office where the injury was discovered. However, the doctor who actually saw me and made the analysis did not see that report because it was sent to the other doctor, for whom the doctor who had seen me was working as an assistant.

The manner in which the report was written was impossible for me to understand. In one excerpt from the report he stated, "We both know that the result from surgery will be the same in two years as it would be without surgery." He never explained to me what he meant by that in the report. In fact, he never said anything whenever I visited him.

In another report, he made a highly insulting statement of such a personal nature that I cannot repeat it here. I brought that statement up at our next appointment. I could see by his manner that he resented my questioning of him. In his report on that appointment, he wrote that I had become angry over his previous report. When I got a copy of that report, I knew this doctor was not caring for me in a professional manner. His arrogance and his ego were too much for me so I decided the next meeting with him would be the last.

When the next appointment arrived, I went to his office and we had another discussion about surgery. I realized any further conversation with this doctor would be useless but I did not tell him this was my last visit. I wanted to get a copy of his report on this last meeting to see what he would write to my insurance provider, which in this case was Worker's Compensation.

He must have realized I was getting copies of his reports every time we had an appointment. When I requested a copy of his report on the last visit, I got only the notes he took during the appointment, which had nothing in them but routine medical jargon.

He was part of the group of doctors I had seen at this same facility before for another matter, as mentioned earlier. I had problems with them then because they kept passing me around to other doctors like a bouncing ball. This was an unfortunate experience because it damaged my view of doctors in general, even more so than before.

I decided I could not deal with doctors in Florida any more because of what I had seen of them up to that point. I did not like feeling that way but until I could meet or discover a doctor I could feel comfortable with, like Dr. Russo in Rhode Island or Dr. Waltz in New York, I felt I had to stay away from Florida doctors when possible.

I decided the best way to approach the decision on whether to have surgery was to contact both Dr. Russo in Rhode Island and Dr. Waltz in New York. I sent them both copies of the myelogram and all the other reports pertaining to my back injury. I asked their advice on what I should do.

Dr. Russo called me and we discussed the findings of the myelogram. Based on what he read in the reports I sent him, he suggested I should give serious consideration to having the surgery.

116

Dr. Russo was a doctor I always felt I could trust and I valued his advice greatly. Dr. Waltz was of the same opinion. In his case, I had the actual X-rays sent to him in New York. The assistant doctor I originally saw in Tampa had also told me that surgical intervention seemed necessary.

This meant that three out of four doctors concurred that the surgery was advisable. With that, it was up to me to decide. I waited a number of months, debating what I should do. In the end, I decided I would have the surgery and Dr. Waltz would be the doctor to perform it. Next came setting up the financing and arranging for the date of the surgery.

The surgery was set for March 27, 1997, at St. Barnabus Hospital in New York. I drove to my father's house in Rhode Island. I would stay there while I awaited my back surgery, which would require that I travel twice. Unlike the installation of the Spinal Cord Stimulator, back surgery was much more involved.

On my first visit, I met with Dr. Waltz about the surgery. He gave me the usual exam for a back surgery candidate. He noted to me that I was fortunate I had not suffered worse injury because nerves in that particular area of the back could have resulted in loss of feeling in my left ankle. He instructed me to go to a blood bank to have blood drawn so it would be available during the surgery if needed. He assured me that was routine.

I got a hotel room that night, then made sure I took care of all the preliminary things needed for back surgery. I went to the blood bank to have blood drawn to ensure an ample supply for the surgery. I also had a CAT scan done. With those errands completed, I then caught a train back to Rhode Island to wait until I had to go back to New York for the back surgery.

I was of course a little nervous about having back surgery. Previously, I had been in a ward at St. Joseph's Hospital that dealt almost exclusively with back injuries as described earlier. There I had met people who had back surgery and did not have very good results. Many of them were back having their second or third surgeries. I certainly did not want to end up like them.

I decided I would tour New York City before my surgery. I reserved a hotel room two nights before being admitted to the hospital. I had to spend at least one night in a hotel anyway because I had to be at the hospital admissions office in the early morning.

I spent my two days roaming around Manhattan in the heart of New York City. I visited Madison Square Garden, Times Square and a number of other unique places. I found an Irish pub on 45th Street that regular New Yorkers visited. I found it to be refreshingly different. I loved the people I met there.

I have always liked meeting all kinds of people. I have found I learn more about life by meeting people different from me in their own little ways.

I walked for miles the two days I was in Manhattan. The dystonia bothered me some but I never let that interfere with trying to enjoy myself. I appreciated that I could walk at all. I knew I would be stuck in a bed in the hospital for five or six days after the surgery so I wanted to get as much exercise as possible beforehand.

I woke up early on the morning of my surgery. I had to check out of the hotel early and catch the subway to St. Barnabus Hospital in the Bronx, which took me about an hour. After arriving at the hospital, I proceeded immediately to the admissions office. I was assigned a hospital room at about 12:00 P.M.

St. Barnabus was a teaching hospital so anyone staying there was always being observed by interns or student doctors. This day was no exception. There was a group of about eight student doctors with an intern. They were usually very friendly and showed a lot of interest in why each patient was in the hospital. I was of special interest because I had the Spinal Cord Stimulator in me to help with the dystonia and I was also going to have major back surgery.

Dr. Waltz showed up later in the afternoon. He briefly discussed what would be happening and told me not to worry. I was a little scared but I had been through so many surgeries that I was getting accustomed to the procedure. Since I would not be able to eat anything after 12:00 A.M., I ate well when dinner arrived.

The nurse in the evening gave me a lot of attention because I would have to be prepared for major surgery. I can remember getting a shot of Demerol that evening. Demerol is a pain medication. The anesthesiologist also visited me; it was routine for him to visit prior to surgery. The anesthesiologist's job was very important in the operating room. I was reminded not to eat or drink anything after midnight.

I reflected on whether I was doing the right thing. I did not really want to do something that would make my suffering worse than it already was. I still feared the effects failed surgery would have on my dystonia. At the same time, I did not really know what would happen in the future if I did not go through with the surgery.

On the other hand, the surgery could have some very positive results. I was particularly hopeful that the surgery would either put an end to the pain I suffered on the right side or at least reduce the pain. Then I would not have to take pain medication and suffer from the side effects associated with those medications. If that happened, I would only have to deal with the effects of the dystonia. Even though the dystonia affected me every day, the medications had it controlled to a level that made life close to normal.

I woke up around 6:00 A.M. I made a point of going to the bathroom. I did not want to have to go just prior to being rolled into the operating room. I of course was not allowed to eat breakfast. The nurse came in and gave me another shot of Demerol.

At around 7:00 A.M., they came to transport me down to surgery. I was moved onto the bed used to transport patients to the operating room. We went down to the area near the operating room where an intravenous line was placed into a vein in my arm by the anesthesiologist. He also put something to relax me in the intravenous line before hooking it up. It did relax me and considering I was there for major back surgery, I of course greatly appreciated that.

Finally, I was wheeled into the operating room. I had been there before when I had the Spinal Cord Stimulator installed in 1988 and during the four revisions performed since that time.

I was moved onto the operating table in a facedown position. At that point, I was set up for the anesthesia. Dr. Waltz talked to me before the anesthesia was applied. He had an uncanny ability of making a person feel very comfortable in the operating room. His reassurance always made me feel much more relaxed.

I could feel them piling on the sheets as I lay there. They finally began administering the anesthesia. After that point, I cannot remember anything.

I woke up in my hospital room after the surgery. I do not remember being in the recovery room although I assume they placed me there for a while because that is normal procedure after a surgery.

Anyone who has had back surgery cannot move around very much and must stay in bed a day or so. I was no exception. Whenever I moved, it hurt. The first thing I noticed when I woke up in the hospital room was pain in my right eye. Apparently, at some time during the surgery, my eye must have been hurt in some way. I told the nurse, then the anesthesiologist came up to my room to check it out. Eventually, an optometrist came to my room also and discovered a tiny bruise on my eye. They gave me a cold pack for it.

I also had trouble urinating. I was then suffering from a painful bruise on my eye and urine retention. Not being able to move around because of the surgery made my situation even more uncomfortable. I also could feel the dystonia movements a little. Being as restricted as I was in moving, the dystonia just increased my discomfort.

The dystonia is always there, affecting me in some small way and making everything in life more difficult just because of its existence.

It was very hard to handle all those problems that cropped up at the same time after my back surgery. Yet like so many other things in life, I just had to get through the difficult period.

Later that day, Dr. Waltz visited me. He told me everything had gone well and he had high hopes the surgery would be effective in reducing my pain. After he left, I kept hoping everything he said would come to pass. If the pain on that right side would just improve by 50%, I would be satisfied.

After lying in a hospital bed for a day, I could not wait to get up and move around. After back surgery, one usually started walking with assistance from a nurse. I was helped out of bed for short escorted walks on the first day after surgery. Before that first day ended, I was getting out of bed on my own to go to the bathroom or to walk around the room. I did not think they wanted me to do that but once I started feeling better, I did not usually follow rules too well. By the next day, I was ready to roam the hallways of the hospital.

I am usually more comfortable moving around than lying down anyway. As I have mentioned earlier, because of the way dystonia affects me, it is hard for me to stay in the same position for a long period of time without getting uncomfortable.

The problem with my eye did get better in a few days. That was a relief for me. I saw an optometrist while still in the hospital. He performed the usual eye tests to be sure my sight had not been damaged.

On the third day after my surgery, I was walking the hallway periodically to get exercise for my back and regain strength. I had a new roommate, a younger guy. He was not the kind of person I felt I could trust. Unfortunately, he stole money and my credit card out of my wallet while I was getting an injection in the operating room. I found out when I got back from receiving the injection but he had been discharged by that time. Luckily, I was able to cancel my credit card before he had a chance to use it.

After five days in the hospital, the day came for me to be released. Wayne, the technologist, came to my hospital room to make sure I got everything I needed before I left. I was given a prescription for antibiotics and some other medications. I actually felt pretty good. Of course, I would not know for a while whether the surgery had been successful.

I took the late train back to Rhode Island. I planned a quick return to Florida from my father's apartment. A few days later, I packed my car for the return to Florida. I said goodbye to family members. I also stopped at my friend Norman's house to see him before I left.

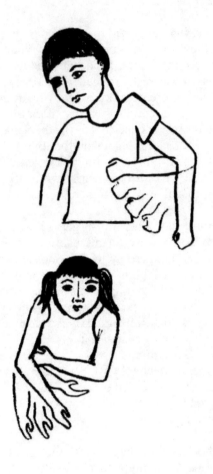

Illustrations above show a boy and a girl in the early stages of early-onset dystonia. The boy is developing movements in his left arm with the raising of his right shoulder. The girl is developing movements in her right arm with rising of her right shoulder. The legs may also be affected in the same fashion depending on the severity of the disease. Control will usually be lost slowly over time.

CHAPTER 18

One might wonder how someone who has just undergone major back surgery and also suffers from a movement disorder can make a 1,300-mile trip back home alone. The answer is simple: When one must get from Point A to Point B, one just does it.

The dystonia did not bother me as much as it used to when driving long distances. Also, when I was in a car alone, I did not have the pressure of hiding the dystonia from anyone. I could move around in almost any direction without the concern of someone watching me and wondering why I moved this way or that way. That amounted to added pressure when someone was around me. It was an instinctive reaction on my part to hide my dystonia from people.

When I drove alone, I was more relaxed. I knew I had to plan my medications carefully though. Since I had taken medications for the dystonia since I was 18, I knew how long they took to go into effect. I also took pain medication. That helped, not only because it reduced the pain, but also because it put me in a more positive frame of mind. Of course, it also could interfere with my driving by making me less alert. Yet in my case, it had a positive effect because without the pain medication, the effects of the pain and the dystonia actually interfered with my ability to drive.

Some doctors might argue against that because they would look at it with a more generalized attitude. However, I have learned from experience that a doctor's advice is not always correct.

I reached home two days after leaving Rhode Island. Dr. Waltz had given me a prescription for post-operative therapy. I had to find a facility nearby to put me on a light exercise program to strengthen my back and improve my flexibility. I found a facility only a mile and a half from my home. I called and made an appointment.

I arrived for my first appointment and was evaluated for the therapy I would need to get my back into shape. It consisted of aquatic therapy at first, followed by some stretching and work on exercise machines. This facility had exercise equipment and a pool to perform exercises in water.

I reported for my first exercise session. The first thing I was asked to do was to walk back and forth in the pool for a specific number of laps. I used only the pool that day. They also had some exercise machines in the water but that first day I did not use them; I only walked back and forth in the pool.

At my second appointment, I did the usual walking back and forth in the pool. I also got to work on the machines in the pool. They slowly built up my pool exercising until I reached a point where I could work out on the machines outside the water. They had an assortment of machines in the exercise area for working different parts of the body. They started me off slowly but I moved through the exercise program quickly and within a month I finished the rehabilitation program.

At that point, my back felt completely healed. I seemed to be back to the same condition I was in before the surgery. However, the pain returned on the right side. At first, it was not that bad but it got progressively worse. By the July following the March surgery, I returned to St. Barnabus Hospital to get some injections in my back similar to cortisone. I received a series of three injections. I got some relief but it did not last long.

I mentioned to Dr. Waltz that I was considering a device called a morphine pump, which was installed internally and which injected morphine directly into the spinal canal. It consisted of a small sack filled with morphine, which was injected into the spinal canal as needed by the patient. The big plus for the morphine pump was that it eliminated the side effects of the drug because it was injected directly into the spinal canal.

Dr. Waltz was a little hesitant to support the pump. However, he suggested trying the morphine patch, a square patch attached to the body with an adhesive on one side while the other side contained morphine. Once the patch was attached to the body, the morphine began to enter into the patient's system through the skin. The patch usually lasted three days. It was then replaced by another patch.

124

The problem with the morphine patch was that it had a lot of side effects. I was staying at my father's house when I first started using it. It did make me feel better at times but during one evening it made me very sick and caused me to vomit almost all night. That happened a couple more times during the period I used the patch.

However, at one time during my use of the patch, a remarkable thing happened. I was sitting on my father's couch when I suddenly realized I felt no pain whatsoever. I was totally stunned by that. As soon as I realized that, I also discovered that I did not feel the dystonia any more. At that moment and for another two days, I felt totally recovered from the dystonia and the pain. That feeling did not last but it was amazing for me to feel that way.

To this day, I have never forgotten those two miraculous days. However, I would never feel improvement like those two days ever again.

I continued on the morphine patch after getting back to Florida but it was inconsistent in its effectiveness. At many times, the drug caused me to feel sick to my stomach. The worst thing about the morphine patch was that it made me feel so drowsy. It was particularly a problem when driving my car; many times, I started nodding off while driving. I had a number of close calls. The one that had the biggest effect was when I almost hit a tractor-trailer truck.

After that incident, I realized I had a choice: I either had to give up driving or give up the morphine patch. I gave up the morphine patch. It would not do me any good to get killed — or even worse, kill someone else — in an automobile accident.

I think the problem with the morphine patch was that depending on the situation, at some times more of the drug penetrated into the skin than at other times. That struck me as a logical conclusion. I think I made a wise decision.

Having failed with the morphine patch, I decided to give the morphine pump a try. Dr. Waltz gave me a referral to a doctor in my home state of Florida. I made an appointment with a doctor in Tampa. It was an 80-mile trip to the facility where I made the appointment. The doctor I saw was not the one Dr. Waltz had referred me to. In fact, he did not even install the morphine pump so my first trip was a total waste. I ended up making an appointment to see a doctor in that same facility that did install morphine pumps.

About a week later, I went for the appointment with that doctor. She was a neurosurgeon and we discussed the pump in some detail. She was not comfortable without getting a second opinion from another doctor in the medical field of rehabilitation. An appointment was made with the rehabilitation doctor the following week. Also, a follow-up appointment was made with the neurosurgeon for the week after that to discuss the rehabilitation doctor's recommendations.

I went to see the rehabilitation doctor. She spent about ten minutes interviewing me. She then went over my records quickly and the appointment ended. I left and traveled the 80 miles back home. The following week, I made the 80-mile trip again to see the neurosurgeon who would install the morphine pump. I was shocked when she told me she had not yet received the report from the rehabilitation doctor and sent me home!

They shared the same office space in the same building on the same floor. I would have thought the doctor would have felt bad that I had traveled 80 miles for nothing for an appointment she specifically made to discuss the rehabilitation doctor's analyses, which she had yet to receive. She made another appointment for the following week. Once again, I made the 80-mile trip home.

The following week, I returned yet again after traveling the same 80 miles I had traveled the previous week. I met again with the neurosurgeon who would be doing the surgery to install the morphine pump. She informed me that the rehabilitation doctor had recommended against installing the morphine pump in me because I was so young.

I was of course disappointed because I was curious about the benefits this device might afford me. I was also angry. I had made five trips to see a total of three different doctors to be told that I was not considered a good candidate for the morphine pump. Total mileage for five round trips, covering a four-week period of time, was 800 miles. I was not upset with the final decision; I was upset because I made so many visits to find out something that could have been done in three visits or less.

126

I left feeling so frustrated because I had accomplished nothing. I was totally dumbfounded and angry that medical doctors who were supposed to be professionals had wasted so much of my time. Their treatment of me bordered on abusive.

At the time all that was happening, I was still using the morphine patch but after that incident I discontinued using it. I went back to a different pain medication. I have never revisited the idea of the morphine pump. I have not ruled it out for the future, however.

As more time passed, it was apparent the back surgery was a failure. I was aware there were no guarantees it would be successful.

The pain continued to increase. I started trying to use the Spinal Cord Stimulator for pain. According to Wayne at Dr. Waltz's office, I usually should use a low frequency level to reduce pain with the stimulator. The general rule of thumb of 20 to 100 Hz was usually effective in the treatment of pain. I worked carefully with Wayne during the latter part of 1997 and early part of 1998 to find a good setting for pain reduction but we did not have much luck.

In April of 1999, something in the internal parts of the stimulator broke down. That meant having another revision, which presented a golden opportunity to try a couple of different things.

The first thing was getting an MRI scan when the stimulator was removed because then there would be no metal in my back. (As I mentioned earlier, I could not have metal in my body when I got an MRI.) That was a little complicated because it meant going into the operating room to have the existing stimulator removed. After removing the stimulator, the surgery would be stopped. Because staples are made of metal, they could not be used so I would be sutured up until the stimulator was reinstalled.

Then the MRI would be performed the next day in the area of the lower back. If time allowed, a second MRI scan would be performed on the cervical area that same day. If not, the second MRI would be performed the next morning.

I brought all of this up to Dr. Waltz in June of 1999 while visiting his office. We also discussed moving the stimulator from its present location in the cervical area to the lower back in the area of the failed back surgery. It was decided the stimulator would be removed from the cervical area and reinstalled in the lower back. In the treatment of lower back pain, that was the most effective area to locate the stimulator.

Next came getting approval from Worker's Compensation. I called Worker's Compensation to discuss the surgery. To my dismay, the individual I had dealt with in the past was seriously ill with cancer and died soon afterward. His replacement was extremely difficult to deal with. He even refused to reimburse me for my mileage expenses for visiting Dr. Waltz in June. Up to that point, I had always been compensated for my trips to New York City to see Dr. Waltz. Eventually, however, I did end up getting reimbursed for those expenses.

The plan with Dr. Waltz was to have the surgery done in July. Plans were made with the hospital and with Dr. Waltz's office. A date was set for my admission into the hospital. The hospital had to know when I was coming in because they needed to make sure the operating room was available.

I kept calling my Worker's Compensation caseworker about sending approval but had no luck. I left messages but never got called back. I found out from Dr. Waltz's office that my Worker's Compensation caseworker had sent a letter to Dr. Waltz, asking him if he could recommend a doctor in Florida. I was amazed that such a letter would be sent to Dr. Waltz at a time when it was critical to get an approval for surgery that had been performed four times before in New York City by Dr. Waltz.

Of course, I realized what was going on. It was not uncommon with some Worker's Compensation providers to hassle people in that fashion. The other caseworker at Worker's Compensation, who had passed away, would have had this approved without a hassle. We always got along fine and always worked things out together in a very human way. This new individual was not a nice guy and I realized if something did not happen soon, I would have to scrap the surgery and retain the services of an attorney.

The day arrived for me to leave for Rhode Island. I would stay with my friend Norman Demers until I went to New York for the surgery. My plan was to leave at 8:00 A.M. Although I was ready to

128

leave at that time, approval for the surgery still had not been received even though it involved only a simple matter of faxing the approval form to the doctor.

I called that morning and could not reach the caseworker handling my Worker's Compensation case. I worked feverishly all morning long, trying to get the approval faxed to Dr. Waltz's office. It was not until 2:00 in the afternoon that I was assured of the approval.

I have no idea why my caseworker at Worker's Compensation was so uncooperative. I guess only he knows that answer.

Finally, I could leave. However, because I was forced to wait so long to get going, it would take me three days to make it to Rhode Island and my friend Norman's apartment. I would arrive in Rhode Island on a Saturday. That meant I would have only Sunday to prepare myself for the trip to New York City and St. Barnabus Hospital since I was scheduled for admission on Monday. That was a lot of aggravation over something that was approved anyway.

We are all human beings in this world and there is no excuse for someone making trouble like this man did.

When I reached Norman's house, I was exhausted. I did not have much time to spend with Norman because of the approval delay. We agreed we would do something together when I got back from New York City.

I arrived in New York City around 10:30 A.M. I immediately got a cab because they were expecting me to arrive at the hospital before noon. I arrived there and raced to the admissions office. Because I arrived a little late, I did not get into a hospital room until later in the afternoon, around 3:00 P.M. That disappointed me a little because I preferred to relax, spend time in my hospital room and prepare myself for surgery on the following day.

I knew I would be spending a few days in the hospital so I got the television hooked up. Wayne, Dr. Waltz's assistant, visited me in my room about an hour after I arrived. We went over everything that would be done during my stay there.

I had undergone surgery at St. Barnabus Hospital so many times that I was referred to as the guy from Florida by the nurses and staff. Supper arrived about 5:30 P.M. I went through the usual preparations

129

before surgery. I relaxed that evening by watching television and taking walks around the hospital hallway.

I was taken down to surgery the next morning. I was prepared for surgery and wheeled into the operating room. This surgery would be a little different form my previous ones. I would be cut open and the internal parts of the Spinal Cord Stimulator would be removed. After it was removed, my incisions would be sutured up and the surgery would be over for that day. As I mentioned earlier, I would be getting an MRI scan of the lower back and also an MRI of the cervical area.

The operation was completed and I was wheeled back to my hospital room after a short time in the recovery room. In my room, I felt good after the surgery. I knew the MRI would be done the next day and that was something I had wanted for a long time. The MRI would tell me in greater detail what was going on in my spine in both the lower back and the cervical area.

The next day, I was wheeled to the room where the MRI would be taken. The last MRI had been done in 1987 as I indicated earlier. The first one to be done this day was of the lower back. I was in more control of my dystonia and better able to control my body before this MRI than I was before the one in 1987. When it was completed, I was wheeled back to my hospital room.

The following day an MRI was done of the cervical area. Once again, I was able to maintain control of my body and the scan was done successfully.

With both MRI's done, I then had to prepare myself for the surgery the following day. It would be different from all the other surgeries because the Spinal Cord Stimulator would be installed in the lower back instead of the cervical area. As noted earlier, that was the area in which the stimulator should be installed to help relieve pain.

The following morning, the Spinal Cord Stimulator was installed in my lower back as scheduled. With the surgery completed, I was wheeled back to my hospital room.

With the stimulator in place, the next objective was to find a setting that would work the best for me in reducing pain. Wayne came to my hospital room to begin testing the stimulator. He listed several specific settings on paper. I would test these different settings, and then Wayne would come back the next day to see how the settings we had selected worked out.

It was normal to go through a 24-hour test period for each setting. In this case, we were trying to speed up the process a little to see if we could get results in a shorter period of time. I would test each setting for a 4-hour period.

With the new settings, I found seemingly significant improvement on one particular setting. When Wayne came back the next day, I told him about that setting. He wrote up some additional settings on some charts and gave them to me to try. I was hoping that finally we might have found something that would reduce the pain more effectively.

With the Spinal Cord Stimulator located in the lower back instead of the cervical area, there was no longer any way to treat the dystonia with the stimulator. However, it was fair to say that the stimulator had not been as effective as I had hoped in treating the dystonia.

I believe I suffered from both Spasmodic Torticollis and Dystonia Musculorum Deformans, (Generalized Dystonia.) The fact was that the medication I took for the dystonia, rather than the stimulator, had pretty much controlled both the Dystonia Musculorum Deformans and the Spasmodic Torticollis. The Spasmodic Torticollis seemed to start becoming a bigger problem after sustaining my first back injury in 1985.

Thinking back to my last two years working for Electric Boat, I can remember some people noticing movement of my right shoulder. That appears to have replaced some of what I had overcome through the use of medications. Of course, it could have been there before. I simply may not have noticed it because the effects of the Dystonia Musculorum Deformans mainly dominated my body.

I am presently receiving massage therapy once a week in one-hour sessions. I find massage therapy helpful in the treatment of my back and it also helps with the dystonia. I can walk into a massage session and leave there walking much straighter than before the therapy. However, there are times when it does not seem to help as much and the relief only lasts a short time.

While the massage therapy works for me, there is no guarantee it will work for everyone. Also, massage therapy is not a permanent solution. Like acupuncture, it wears off after a short time. If I could get massage therapy every day, I would probably notice significant improvement in my back pain and perhaps some improvement in the dystonia. Of course, that would be expensive.

I also have been training at a gym, doing three aerobics classes a week. The benefits of the aerobics come from the stretching exercises. With a bad back, I know I must keep moving because a bad back can tighten up the body and cause movements to become more restricted. With all the moves in aerobics, the body is being worked all over and loosens up muscles so the body can move more freely. It of course has a positive psychological effect also. I feel better about myself and that helps me feel more relaxed. Feeling more relaxed benefits both my back and the dystonia.

At present, I am still using the Spinal Cord Stimulator. I just had another revision of the stimulator on February 5, 2002, at Our Lady of Mercy Hospital in New York City. Previously, I had the four-electrode system installed. This time I had the eight-electrode system installed. I find that with eight electrodes the range of stimulation is far greater. Now I can feel stimulation in a much broader area, increasing my ability to treat pain in a larger area of the body.

I also have the newest transmitter developed by Advanced Neuromodulation Systems (ANS). This new transmitter gives me ease of operation I never experienced with the older one. Adjustment to my stimulation can be made right at my fingertips. I am presently still in the testing phase with the eight-electrode system but I already have experienced significant reduction in pain from both the back injury and to a somewhat lesser extent from the dystonia.

I do not use pain medication unless I feel I absolutely must. If I am going somewhere special, I will take one just to help me enjoy what I am doing or to keep me from feeling excessive pain.

I am reasonably content with my present situation with the dystonia. It is under control with the medications I take. As I get

132

older, I want to be able to enjoy what is left of my life relatively free of pain. I am not a quitter and I look forward to a better future.

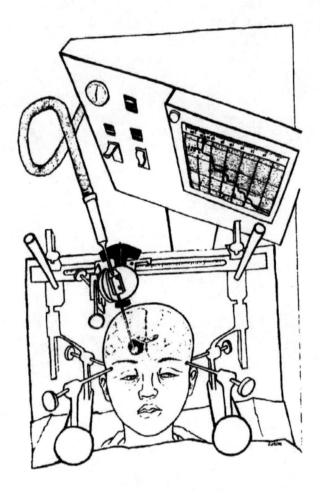

The illustration above shows a female child with a severe case of, Dystonia Musculorum Deformans, with her head shaved and held in a vice undergoing Thalamic Brain Surgery. She will be awake during the entire procedure. This is necessary because the doctor performing the surgery needs feedback from the patient to know if the patient feels any relief from the surgery.

REFLECTIONS

Dystonia, a movement disorder, is considered a rare illness. Many doctors do not even know what it is. The name is not well known like Parkinson's disease, another movement disorder. Yet dystonia patients can be found all over the world.

Centuries ago, people were put to death when they had symptoms similar to dystonia. Women were called witches and were sometimes burned alive. Many of those people may have had dystonia.

Today, people are not burned alive because they have this affliction. Instead in many cases, they are misdiagnosed. While this is not as bad, it is certainly similar in some ways to the thinking of centuries ago. When one cannot explain a human affliction, one immediately questions the person's mental condition.

How in our modern society can this kind of thing happen? Remember when AIDS (Acquired Immune Deficiency Syndrome) first appeared about two decades ago? There were all sorts of misconceptions about the disease including how one could contract it. Today, we know a lot more about AIDS than we knew when this disease first appeared.

Having full-blown AIDS usually leads to death. However, dystonia does not lead to death unless a person has an extremely severe case. I have not found any instances of a person dying as a direct result of dystonia.

Dystonia comes in many different forms. Some forms are worse than others. I have a form called Dystonia Musculorum Deformans, more commonly known as Generalized Dystonia. I also suffer from Spasmodic Torticollis. Since the medical profession has individualized dystonia into a number of different forms based on the area and muscles affected, I think it might be fair to say I suffer from Generalized Dystonia for the most part, with the lower extremities controlled more from medication than the Spasmodic Torticollis.

135

My dystonia affects many parts of my body. I have experienced involuntary movements in my left arm, right arm, left leg and right leg. My left ankle still curls up a little but I can straighten it out with little effort.

There is a twisting motion in my lower back that I still experience to this day, although it is controlled very well by the medications I take.

While I have good control of my hands now, I had trouble writing when I was in high school because I experienced some lack of coordination in my fingers. I still experience that today but at a reduced level. I also suffer from movement in my right shoulder and my neck.

Early onset dystonia, such as Generalized Dystonia, is brutal because it increases in intensity and grows progressively worse over time. In my case, I would gradually lose control of one muscle, then another. It did not really bother me that much in the beginning because it did not affect me enough to alter my everyday life.

However, as my walking deteriorated, its effect on my everyday life began to increase. As I became aware that I was walking in an abnormal way, I began to feel embarrassment over the way I walked, something that such a young boy did not normally experience. I had to deal with this developing problem at a very young age. I believe young children experiencing this kind of problem need love and comfort from their parents. My parents were perplexed about what to do for me.

During the first year or two, when I went to doctors at the clinic they only saw a walking problem. No one had any idea at that time that the illness would evolve into almost total incapacitation.

When the movements spread to other muscles and other limbs of my body, having difficulty with walking was no longer the only problem. Then I began developing problems with sitting. That was a particular concern because people do a lot of things in their everyday lives while sitting. Imagine sitting down in a chair to read a book. This is a simple enough thing to do.

However, as my dystonia progressed, it became difficult to sit in a chair comfortably and read a book. Eventually, I was forced to read a book on my bed while lying on my stomach. Even then, it was uncomfortable.

Another element of sitting was when I was tired and wanted to rest. I sat in a chair and rested my body. Yet as my illness progressed, I reached a point where that was not possible. I constantly had to wiggle around in my chair, trying to get comfortable. That was the point of my life when I began countering the uncontrolled movements by using the muscles I could control.

Soon after the problem of sitting comfortably developed, so did the problem of standing. During my early onset of dystonia, I never completely lost the ability to stand. However, as the illness progressed, standing became difficult. The one redeeming thing about standing was that as long as I had something to lean on and I was in a position where I could shift my weight around, I was okay. Again, the secret was to counter uncontrolled movements with muscles I could control.

In the earlier stage of my dystonia, I could still run even though I struggled when walking. I started losing my ability to run about the same time I was trying to play baseball and started falling after swinging the bat. Shortly after that, I started falling on my way to first base. In essence, I first developed a problem with standing, which was closely followed by difficulty with running.

I mentioned earlier about reading a book while lying on my stomach on the bed because of the difficulty I experienced when trying to read while sitting in a chair. As the dystonia progressed, it eventually started affecting me more and more while lying in bed.

When I went to bed at night, the dystonia caused excessive movements that made sleeping very difficult. To sleep, I had to counter the movements by placing my body in different positions on the bed. Many times I lay on my right side with my left leg over and forward of my right leg. Other times, it was the opposite. Other times, I lay on my stomach with my right leg under my left leg on the left side of my body. When lying on my back, I frequently crossed my left leg over my right leg to the right side of my body as far as it would go. I did the same with the other side of my body, with the left leg placed as far as it would go. I did all these kinds of things to find reasonable comfort. Today, however, this is rarely a problem.

When I was in 8th grade, I would stop at the water fountain to get a drink of water and at the same time use that time to regroup myself to help me get to my next class. Stopping at the water fountain and stopping to tie my shoes were different ways I used to overcome dystonia and to function in school.

Gaining control of my body was like a chess game. For every involuntary move, there was a voluntary move. It was a war between the controlled muscles versus the uncontrolled muscles.

TREATMENTS FOR DYSTONIA TODAY

Drug Therapy

There are a number of treatments for dystonia sufferers today. Also, there are many medications available to dystonia patients.

In a book by Eugene Smith, **Dystonia: The Disease that Distorts**, he interviewed several dystonia patients using medications. Many showed considerable improvement through the use of various medication combinations.

I presently use three medications to control my dystonia: Artane, Kemadrin and Klonopin.

In Mr. Smith's book, those he interviewed spoke of the side effects many of the medications caused. In the case of Artane, many experienced some memory loss. I have noticed that I too experience that kind of reaction. In one particular case, a patient spoke of experiencing drowsiness using Klonopin. I have experienced drowsiness from both Artane and Klonopin.

Of course, the drowsiness also comes from some of the other medications combined with Klonopin. Most of these medications are muscle relaxants or tranquilizers so drowsiness should be expected. The Klonopin has been helpful with pain, as well as the movements, when combined with the other medications.

I recently discovered something that has helped me overcome some of my drowsiness. Years ago, I stopped drinking coffee with caffeine in it because I knew caffeine could cause an irritation in the nervous system. A few months ago, I purchased flavored coffee with caffeine. To my surprise, the caffeine made me feel wide-awake and I overcame some of the drowsiness. It was not a cure-all but it was effective in offsetting the drowsiness.

While I do not like caffeine in my body, I find this to be a fair trade-off. It does not work all day long but does provide some relief from the drowsiness through the morning.

Other medications used in controlling dystonia are Tegretol, Cogentin, Baclofen, Neurontin, Topamax, Risperdal, Neptazane, Tetrabenezine and many others. I have used both Tegretol and Cogentin in the past.

The first time I tried Tegretol was about 13 years ago. It did not aid me with the dystonia even though my doctor at the time expected it to be very helpful. He was surprised when I told him it had not helped me. I tried it again about ten months ago and still did not note any improvement from the dystonia but it did seem to help a little with the pain from my back injury. I discontinued it because it could be harmful to the body when taken over an extended period of time.

Kemadrin appears to be a key drug for me. Combined with Artane, it has been the most effective medication for me.

Botox

Botox is botulinum-toxin, which is injected into the muscle. What this substance docs is block nerve impulses as they travel from the brain to the muscle. Botulinum toxin is actually a poison. It is injected into the muscle with carefully monitored dosages so that its poisonous effects are significantly reduced. The toxin usually lasts three to four months before another injection is made. This is one of the most successful treatments of dystonia available today. I am not a good candidate for this kind of treatment at this time but would not hesitate to use it in the future if the need were to arise.

Botox is also used for the treatment of wrinkles. The recent publicity regarding this treatment for wrinkles is unfortunate because it has been used for the treatment of dystonia for a number of years now. The fact that so much publicity has occurred for its use for wrinkles while there has been virtually no publicity regarding its success in treating illnesses such as dystonia is unfortunate. If the same media coverage were to be afforded to the treatment of dystonia the publicity would be very helpful in raising money for dystonia

140

research. The media should be chastised for this oversight.

Baclofen Pump

The Baclofen Pump is a method of delivering the drug, baclofen directly into the spinal fluid. The pump system consists of a catheter and a pump. The pump consists of a round metal disk about the size of a hockey puck that is surgically placed under the skin in the area of the abdomen. The pump stores and releases the prescribed amounts of medication through a catheter into the spinal canal. The pump is programmed to release a specific amount of baclofen based on the patient's needs.

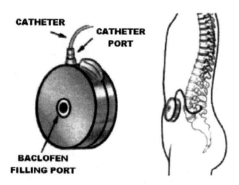

INTRATHECAL BACLOFEN PUMP SYSTEM

Cryothalamectomy
(Brain Surgery)

This is surgery performed in the thalamus area of the basal ganglia located in the rear of the brain. This is a very delicate operation and should always be the last resort reserved for a person with a very serious case of dystonia. The patient's head has to be clamped in a vise to keep it from moving. A small incision is made in the scalp, exposing the bone underneath. An electric drill is used to bore a dime-sized hole in the skull. After that, a complicated process is begun to prepare for the insertion of a probe into the thalamus area of the brain.

The probe is then slowly inserted into the tiny hole in the cortex of the brain until the tip rests a specific distance below the surface of the brain. Liquid nitrogen enters into the probe until the tip of the probe reaches temperatures far below zero; that freezes an area about the size of a pea. The freezing process causes cessation of the function of the small region where the tip of the probe is located.

The patient is kept awake during the surgery so the surgeon can receive feedback from the patient regarding improvements felt in the areas affected during the freezing process. If, for example, a patient's hand and fingers are in a fixed position, the surgeon will ask the patient during the freezing process if he or she can move the hand and fingers. The freezing temperature will be increased until optimal results are reached. This surgery is also used in the treatment of Parkinson's disease. Please look at the illustration on page 134. This illustration shows what is involved in the surgery in significant detail.

Spinal Cord Stimulation

Besides the medications I take, I also have utilized the Spinal Cord Stimulator with mixed results. It was originally installed to treat my dystonia; for that, the lead was installed in the cervical area. If it is being used for lower back pain, the lead is installed in the lower lumbar region of the back. The stimulator has been used very successfully in the treatment of my back pain. Since it was moved from my cervical area to my lower back, I am presently being treated exclusively for pain with it. Yet the success since this change in 1999 has been inconsistent. At times, it provides relief for me but on other occasions it is not effective. Sometimes it even increases the pain. The key to success is finding the proper setting.

I frequently discover that when I find a setting that is beneficial, it always seems to become ineffective or less effective over time. This forces me to change to settings that have been used before with some success. I often find myself going from one setting to the next in search of relief. The testing process is difficult because there are so many combinations of settings that can be used. However, it does work on back pain and I would highly recommend it to any prospective patient.

The stimulator has also been successfully used in the treatment of cerebral palsy, post-traumatic brain injury, spinal cord injury and degenerative diseases. This is not to say it will work in every such case but it has worked for many individuals suffering from these debilitating illnesses.

I have provided for the reader an illustration on page 100 of both the implanted part of the Spinal Cord Stimulator as well as the external antenna and transmitter.

Selective Denervation

This procedure, developed in the early 1980s, involves cutting the specific nerves in the muscle group involved-in the dystonia condition. Cutting the nerves weakens them permanently and cannot be reversed. An electromyography (EMG) is used to correctly identify the muscles contributing to the symptoms. This method is primarily used in the treatment of Cervical Dystonia, (Spasmodic Torticollis)

Pallidotomy
(Brain Surgery)

This surgery involves destruction of part of the globus pallidus located in the part of the brain involved with the control of movement. A wire probe is inserted into the Gpi. Once its exact location is confirmed the probe heats surrounding tissue by emission of radio waves destroying the tissue. This surgery is more commonly used in the treatment of Parkinson's disease and is only recommended in more severe cases of dystonia.

THE LATEST IN DYSTONIA TREATMENT AND RESEARCH

Deep Brain Stimulation

Deep brain stimulation (DBS) uses an implanted electrode to deliver continuous high-frequency electrical stimulation to either the thalamus, the globus pallidus or the subthalamic nucleus, another part of the brain controlling movement. An electrode is placed into a specific structure of the brain. The DBS is programmed to send tiny electrical impulses to the brain to control tremor. High frequency stimulation of cells in these areas actually shuts them down, helping to rebalance control messages throughout the movement control centers in the brain. It is the same basic principle as that of the Spinal Cord Stimulator. Patients can turn the DBS off or on through the use of a small magnet passed across the area of the implant.

In 1997, the Food and Drug Administration approved the use of deep brain stimulation for the treatment of essential tremor and Parkinson's disease. It is presently being studied in the treatment of dystonia patients.

Gene Research

In 1997 a research team from Massachusetts General Hospital along with others identified and cloned the gene responsible for early -onset dystonia, an inherited neurological disorder that begins in childhood. The discovery is the result of more than 15 years of research and contains important clues that could lead to better understanding of the disease and a cure. While a cure may be years away this discovery is a major breakthrough in the study of dystonia and its prevention.

It is estimated that 50,000 people in the United State and Canada are affected by early-onset dystonia. Symptoms of early-onset dystonia usually begin in the legs or arms and spread to the rest of the body, causing it to twist thus distorting movement and forcing the patient to loss control of the body. More severe cases can confine a patient to a wheelchair or even causing them to be bedridden.

The gene is called DYT1. In their research they discovered that almost all sufferers of early-onset dystonia are attributed to the same mutation. This is important because in other genetic diseases there are different mutations in the same gene.

Not all people who have the gene develop early-onset dystonia. If a carrier of the mutated gene does not develop the gene by the age of 28 they are virtually assured of not developing the symptoms.

I was tested for the gene in March of 2002 and was found to not carry this gene. My development of dystonia is a mystery. While most patients with this disease have the gene there are a small number of dystonia patients who do not have the gene but still have early-onset dystonia.

DIFFERENT FORMS OF DYSTONIA

PRIMARY (Idiopathic Torsion) DYSTONIA

In the majority of cases known as focal dystonias, the dystonia only affects one muscle group.

SPASMODIC TORTICOLLIS (Cervical Dystonia)

This most common of the focal dystonias involves the neck. The muscle spasms cause the neck to twist to one side (torticollis), forwards (antecollis) or backwards (retrocollis). The neck may pull, turn or jerk; eventually, it may be held permanently in one direction. See illustrations on page 72 and 80

BLEPHAROSPASM

This is a focal dystonia of the muscles around the eyes. Early symptoms may be uncontrollable blinking, especially in bright light. Sometimes spasms can become so frequent that the eyelids remain tight shut, making the patient unable to see even though the eyes and vision are normal.

ORMANDIBULAR DYSTONIA

This focal dystonia involves the muscles of the jaw, tongue and mouth. The spasms may cause the mouth to pull open or shut tight. Speech and swallowing may be distorted.

CRANIAL DYSTONIA

Cranial dystonia is a focal dystonia that is a combination of blepharospasm and oromandibular dystonia. Other names used to describe the same combination are Meige syndrome and Breughel syndrome.

LARYNGEAL DYSTONIA

This focal dystonia of the speech muscles of the throat causes strained or forced speech (sometimes called spasmodic dysphonia) or inability to speak in more than a whisper (whispering dysphonia). Some patients with cranial dystonia may also have laryngeal dystonia.

WRITER'S CRAMP

This focal dystonia of the hand causes spasms or contraction of the hand and forearm muscles to occur while writing. Other focal dystonias of the hand include typist's cramp, pianist's cramp and other musician's cramps, as well as golfer's cramp and other sports cramps).

GENERALIZED DYSTONIA
(Dystonia Musculorum Deformans)

This is a form of dystonia that affects many parts of the body. In these cases, the cause of the dystonia is unknown. It usually starts in childhood in one limb and eventually spreads to involve many parts of the body, including the back, neck and arms. This is commonly called an early onset-dystonia. See illustrations on page 6, 63, and 64.

DOPA-RESPONSIVE DYSTONIA (Segawa's Disease)

Perhaps the most rare dystonia, this is found mainly in Japan, Europe and the United States. It usually starts in childhood or adolescence with dystonia and stiffness similar to that seen in Parkinson's disease and symptoms often worsen as the day progresses. Treatment with the drug L-Dopa may almost completely relieve the symptoms and effectiveness appears to last indefinitely.

SECONDARY (Symptomatic) DYSTONIA

In this type of dystonia, the symptoms are due to small areas of brain damage. The dystonia is often segmental, generalized or hemi-dystonia. The damage can be caused by reduced oxygen around the time of birth (cerebral palsy), by injury to the brain or by small strokes or tumors.

AXIAL DYSTONIA

This form of dystonia is manifested by flexed deformity of the trunk and shoulders. It can also cause speech and swallowing difficulty. See illustration on page 106.

APPENDIX

National Library of Medicine – 8600 Rockville Pike, Bethesda, Maryland 20894; Phone: 888-FIND-NLM ; Website: http://www.nlm.nih.gov

WebMD Health – 669 River Drive, Elwood Park, New Jersey 07407; Website: http://www.webmd.com

Dystonia and the Alexander Technique – CCAT@Alexandertec.u-net.com

National Institute of Neurological Disorders and Stroke – NIH Neurological Institute, P.O. Box 5801, Bethesda, Maryland 20824; Phone: 1-800-352-9424; Email: Neuroscience@NIH.gov

Dystonia Medical Research Foundation – One East Wacker Drive, Suite 2430, Chicago, Illinois 60601-1905; Email: dystonia@dystonia-foundation.org

Society for Neuroscience – 11 Dupont Circle N.W., Suite 500, Washington, D.C. 20036; Phone: 202-462-9740; Email: info@sfn.org

Massachusetts General Hospital Neurogenetics DNA Diagnostics Laboratory – Contact: Melanie Collins; Phone: 617-726-5721

Arizona Dystonia Institute – Scottsdale Memorial North Medical Plaza 3, 10210 North Ninety-Second Street, Suite 300, Scottsdale, Arizona 85258; Phone: 480-860-1222

Fazzini Parkinson's Disease and Dystonia – Botulinum Injection Center, 345 E. 37th Street, Suite 317C; New York, New York 10016; Phone: 212-983-1370; Website: www.parkinsons-botulinum.com/about.html-10k

150

Dystonia Inc. – P.O. Box 28, Mukwonago, WI 53149

The Dystonia Society – 46/47 Britton Street, London, England ECIM 5UJ; Phone: 020-7490-5671

Penn State Neurosurgery – Penn State Milton S. Hershey Medical Center, P.O. Box 850, M.C. H110, Hershey, Pennsylvania 17033; Phone: 717-531-3858

We Move – 204 West 84th Street, New York, New York 10024; Phone: 1-800-437-MOV2; Email: wemove@wemove.org; Website: www.wemove.org

National Organization for Rare Disorders, Inc. – P.O. Box 8923, New Fairfield, Connecticut 06812-8923; Phone: 203-746-6518

National Spasmodic Dysphonia Association – One East Wacker Drive, Suite 2430, Chicago, Illinois 60601-1905; Phone: 800-795-NSDA; Email: NSDA@dysphonia.org

Advanced Neuromodulation Systems (ANS) – 6501 Windcrest Drive 100, Piano, Texas 75024; Phone: 800-727-7846

The Victim Is Always the Same by I. S. Cooper – Publisher: W.W. Norton & Company, Inc., 500 Fifth Avenue, New York, New York 10110; Phone: 212-869-0856

Dystonia, the Disease That Distorts by Eugene Smith – Publisher: Peanut Butter Publishing, 226 2nd Avenue West, Seattle, Washington 98119; Website: http//www.pbpublishing.com

Bachmann-Strauss Dystonia & Parkinson Foundation – Phone: 212-241-5614; Website: www.dystonia-parkinsons.org; Email: Bachmann.Strauss@mssm.edu

Mayo Clinic – 4500 San Pablo Road, Jacksonville, Florida 32224; Phone: 904-953-2000

"Cervical cord stimulation in the treatment of athetosis and dystonia" by J. M. Waltz, J. A. Davis, S. Fahn, & D. Caine – Published in *Experimental Therapeutics of Movement Disorders*, 1983, pp. 225-237; Publisher: Raven Press, New York

Stanley Fahn, M.D.H. – Houston Merritt Professor, Dept. of Neurology, Columbia University, College of Physicians and Surgeons, New York, New York

Index

Feedback 134, 142
Fixed Position 88, 89, 107, 109, 142
Flexibility 109, 123
Florida 101, 103, 105, 115, 116, 121, 125, 128, 129
Flow Chart 98
Fluoroscope 97
Food and Drug Administration 145
Freezing Process 142
Frequency 98, 99, 127, 145
Frequency Adjustments 98
Frequency Level 98, 127

G

Gene 145, 146
General Anesthesia 91
General-Dynamics Corporation 73
Generalized Dystonia 7, 45, 83, 88, 91, 106, 131, 135, 136, 148
Globus Pallidus 144, 145
Goalie 46
Grotesque 50, 56
Groton, Connecticut 70, 73
Guardrail 51, 52, 53
Gym Class 34, 42, 57, 58, 65, 66

H

Handicapped 12
Herniated Disk 114

Homeroom Teacher 33, 34, 45
Hospital Room 86, 90, 91, 92, 118, 120, 27, 37, 56, 129, 130
HZ 98

I

Ice Skate 45
Images 84
Implant 99, 108, 114, 145
Implanted Parts 114
Implanted Receiving Unit 108
Incapacitated 6, 14
Incapacitation 136
Injection 86, 114, 121, 124
Instinctively 41, 57, 84
Internal Parts 100, 105, 127, 130
Intravenously Fed Robaxin 86
Interns 118
Involuntary Movement 6, 7, 22, 30, 39, 41, 45, 57, 58, 84, 136

J

Jogging 66
Junior College 70, 75

K

Kemadrin 60, 139, 140
Klonopin 139